Building One Team

I0875931

Building One Team: Cultivating Psychological Safety and Behaviors for Healthy Teams offers a practical and research-backed roadmap to fostering psychological safety and strengthening the behavioral dynamics that shape healthy, high-performing teams.

Drawing on research in the construction industry—a sector known for its high-stress, high-stakes environments—the book explores what it takes to move from fragmented efforts to cohesive, high-performing collaboration. It introduces the concept of "One Team" as a way to understand how psychological safety and everyday team behaviors come together to create healthier, more united teams. Grounded in real-world stories and supported by research data and case studies, the book provides activities, tools, and frameworks that teams in any industry can adapt to their unique challenges and contexts. Each chapter includes structured exercises, discussion prompts, and facilitation tips that can be used immediately in team meetings, huddles, or training.

Written for construction project managers, safety professionals, project executives, and team leaders in high-stakes industries, this essential guide will help readers improve coordination, strengthen trust, and help their teams truly work as one.

Dr. Sulyn Gomez Villanueva brings together expertise in psychological safety, team dynamics, and lean construction through her work at DPR Construction. Her recent work with DPR's Self-Perform Work team focuses on developing processes and resources that create stronger pathways for craftworker voice, participation, and recognition—helping ensure that craftworkers are heard, engaged, and treated as integral members of project teams.

Dr. Glenn Ballard is a research associate with the Project Production Systems Laboratory at the University of California, Berkeley. He co-founded the International Group for Lean Construction and the Lean Construction Institute and developed the Last Planner System, a widespread planning approach used on lean projects. He has played a foundational role in adapting lean thinking to project delivery and has profoundly shaped the theory and practice of lean in the construction industry.

"This is an important and deeply practical contribution to the growing body of work on psychological safety. Drawing on vivid stories from the field and rigorous inquiry, *Building One Team* identifies concrete behaviors, tools, and routines that leaders and teams can use right away to make speaking up viable in construction and other work projects. Construction as a context has long been associated with toughness and silence—but this book shows not only that candor, care, and high standards can coexist, but in fact they are mutually reinforcing. This only happens when leaders are intentional about how work gets done. The result is a compelling, actionable roadmap for building cultures where learning is continuous, dignity is non-negotiable, and people can do their best thinking together."

Amy C. Edmondson, *Novartis Professor of Leadership and Management, Harvard Business School*

"After 30 years in the construction industry, few books have shifted my perspective the way *Building One Team* has. This work expands psychological safety far beyond its traditional link to safety, clearly showing its impact on quality, performance, learning, and trust across entire project teams. Grounded in real-world experience and rich with actionable insights, this book sets a new standard for how leaders build teams that perform better—and work better—together."

Todd Mercer, *Senior Vice President, Webcor Builders*

"This book provides the tools to recognize and cultivate psychologically safe, healthy teams, regardless of industry. Through concepts such as active listening, judgment-free dialogue, and accountability through follow-through, it challenges long-standing norms that suppress voice. Drawing on data and personal stories, this book makes a compelling case that psychological safety belongs alongside physical safety as a core element of the work experience. The results, demonstrated through research and practice, speak for themselves."

Ben Hunt, *Safety Leader of Self-Perform Work Northeast Region, DPR Construction*

"Psychological safety is the foundation of any high-performing team, especially when attempting to create a 'no rank in the room' relationship amongst team members. This book is an essential read for any leader and team that strives to create a high-performing team where every voice matters, regardless of rank. Through concepts such as Respecting People, Active Learning, Active Caring, Active Listening, and Making Reliable Promises, to name a few, the authors explain how those concepts strongly support the creation of a high-performing team. Lastly, the book reminds us that a 'Healthy Team' does not mean a team without tension, disagreement, or breakdowns. Instead, it provides tools for teams to utilize when facilitating difficult conversations. This book is a true tool for becoming 'One Team.'"

Chris Littler, *Northeast Region Safety Leader, DPR Construction*

Building One Team

Cultivating Psychological Safety and Behaviors for Healthy Teams

Sulyn Gomez Villanueva and Glenn Ballard

Routledge
Taylor & Francis Group
NEW YORK AND LONDON

Designed cover image: Shutterstock

First published 2027
by Routledge
605 Third Avenue, New York, NY 10158

and by Routledge
4 Park Square, Milton Park, Abingdon, Oxon, OX14 4RN

Routledge is an imprint of the Taylor & Francis Group, an informa business

ISBN: 978-1-041-22979-7 (hbk)
ISBN: 978-1-041-22455-6 (pbk)
ISBN: 978-1-003-73486-4 (ebk)

DOI: 10.1201/9781003734864

Typeset in Times New Roman
by Apex CoVantage, LLC

Healthy teams do not happen by accident. They are built, one interaction at a time, through the everyday ways people speak up, listen, care for one another, learn, and follow through together. Most of us recognize the value of these behaviors. The challenge is putting them into practice consistently, especially when pressure rises and priorities compete. Building One Team *offers practical pathways for strengthening these behaviors and the foundation that makes them possible: psychological safety. At its core, this book is about creating the kind of team you would want for someone you love—a team where people can contribute fully, stay whole, and do great work together.*

To Emilia Juliette and Victoria,

my greatest joy, my deepest love, and my daily reminder of what truly matters.

Always by your side,

Mom

Contents

Foreword

No passion so effectively robs the mind of all its powers of acting and reasoning as fear.
(Edmund Burke, 1756)

It is a great honor to write this foreword. This book is an important addition to the subject of psychological safety and the new definitions of leadership that best facilitate the formation and work of high-performing, collaborative teams. The Edmund Burke quote, which also prefaces Amy Edmondson's book, *The Fearless Organization*, remains as true and urgent now as it was in 1756 and tells us something important: fear continues to shape the way people think, act, and work together.

This book is about working together. That sentence sounds almost too simple to require examination. And yet, if you have spent any meaningful time in the design and construction industry, you already know that working together is among the most complex things human beings attempt. And fear is often the invisible force standing in the way of collaborative performance.

In all we do, we carry the full weight of what it means to be human: the desire to be seen as competent, the fear of judgment or rejection, the instinct toward self-protection, the desire to belong, and the quiet hope that our contributions matter. These are not weaknesses or character flaws. Fear is a biological inheritance. When human beings perceive social threat—the threat of judgment, rejection, or humiliation—the brain responds with the same neurological cascade it evolved to handle physical danger. Blood flows away from the prefrontal cortex, the seat of complex thinking and creative problem-solving, and toward the systems designed for immediate survival. These forces are part of the operating conditions of every team that has ever tried to create anything.

What the authors ask—and what they have helped us answer—is a profoundly practical question: given those conditions, given real human beings with real fears and real relationships and real stakes, how do we actually get something done together? Not just adequately but superlatively, reliably, with integrity, and with the kind of trust and relationships that bring intent and outcome into much closer alignment. This question is the heart of what is written in these pages. It is a question about the gap between intention and outcome—about what a team sets out to do and what it actually delivers. Every framework, every tool, and every behavioral practice mentioned herein is ultimately aimed at narrowing that gap. And in doing so, the authors remind us that our greatest challenges are often not merely technical but deeply human.

In any framework that depends on reliable commitments from interdependent people, these dynamics are not minor issues. Fear is a direct threat to the system itself. Therefore, honesty and trust in this context are not merely feelings. They are the structural, load-bearing elements of a collaborative system. When they fail, the system fails.

In the early stages of building psychological safety, honest communication feels as though it requires significant conscious exertion. Admitting uncertainty takes courage. Raising a concern in a meeting requires bravery and overcoming real resistance. These are acts of individual will, and they are exhausting to sustain against a culture that has not yet shifted. The question then becomes: How do individual acts of courage become organizational norms?

The authors of this book have spent years working with, and thinking about, this question. They have seen what it looks like when teams have real psychological safety: the quiet confidence of a project in good health, and the cumulative trust that builds between people who have learned they can count on each other. They have also seen what it looks like without it: the cascade of reactive work, eroded relationships, and the sometimes horrendous overtime and rework that might have been prevented if someone had said what they actually knew, earlier in the process.

What you hold in your hands now is a practical guide to the human behaviors and conditions that either drive or erode the psychological safety necessary for the success of high-performing teams. It is not a book of abstract theory. It is a book of insights and tools—behavioral, cultural, and systemic—built from the experience of practitioners who have done this work in the field, on real projects, with real teams under real pressure.

The complexity of human collaboration is not going away. The stakes, risks, and difficulties in design and construction are not getting smaller. But genuinely high-performing, psychologically safe, trust-rich teams are real. This has been demonstrated. They can be built—not as easily as one might wish, and they require bravery, the right understanding, the right practices, and the sustained commitment of leaders who are willing to go first. This book will help you build them.

Sean Graystone
Lean Design and Construction Coach and Trainer

A Note From Sulyn

Our book, *Building One Team*, is grounded in the belief that high-performing, healthy teams do not happen by chance; they are shaped by behavioral dynamics rooted in psychological safety. "One Team" speaks to unity—a mindset of shared purpose, trust, and care. We propose that this unity is not static but is cultivated through daily actions: how team members speak up, listen, plan, learn, and support one another. This book explores how teams can cultivate those dynamics through practical tools, stories, and conversations that help them move from fragmented ways of working to more cohesive, purpose-driven collaboration.

When we say "healthy teams," we mean teams that can hold each other accountable without fear—where candor and care coexist, commitments do not come at the expense of relationships, and performance does not come at the expense of people.

As we explore what it takes to build a true One Team, we begin with a concept at the center of healthy teamwork—psychological safety. I believe that psychological safety is what helps turn a group of talented individuals into a team that can adapt, innovate, and grow together as one. Without it, even the most skilled people can default to silence, self-protection, or burnout—retreating into something I call "Survival Mode."

Survival Mode Is Real

I took my first official job at 17 as a quality control engineer for a steel subcontractor. Since then, I have been fortunate to work across different teams and roles where it felt safe to be myself—something I did not fully appreciate early in my career.

I use the word "fortunate" intentionally because I have come to understand that this experience is far from the norm. For many, feeling psychologically safe at work is not an expectation but rather a privilege, something fragile, inconsistent, or even out of reach. Although I have been part of remarkable teams that allowed me to feel safe, I also know firsthand what it is like to work in environments where I did not. The toll, both mental and physical, can be profound. It shows up as the stress you carry home, the exhaustion of constantly second-guessing yourself, and the quiet loneliness of wondering whether you are good enough. In writing this book, I revisited those memories, which ground many of the reflections in the chapters ahead. My hope is that these pages offer inspiration, empowerment, connection, and perhaps even healing so you can start contributing fully to your teams without having to armor up first.

As a researcher, I have collaborated with a number of teams. At the beginning of each chapter, I share snapshots of these experiences—the *"aha" moments* that shaped my understanding of what it takes to build a true One Team and inspired the development of this book. These moments made me pause and see more clearly why some teams thrive while others quietly struggle.

I found that when people do not feel psychologically safe, they often slip into this survival mode, just as I had at certain points in my own journey. When survival mode is ON, the goal shifts—it is no longer about contributing, learning, or growing but simply about getting through the day. People protect themselves by staying quiet, filtering their ideas, and choosing "safe" versions of the truth—even when candor would help the team see problems sooner and respond better. Over time, this does not just exhaust individuals; it creates unhealthy teams: slower learning, more hidden risk, more rework, and less trust. Psychological safety is not a "nice-to-have" but rather part of what allows people to contribute fully and teams to grow stronger together.

While I used the word *fortunate* on purpose earlier, I believe it is only fair—and deeply human—to treat others in ways that help them feel psychologically safe and truly valued as members of their teams. I am embracing this idea, hoping it becomes the new normal. When people feel safe, seen, and valued, they do not just comply—they commit. They look out for one another, speak up while there is still time to prevent rework, coordinate earlier instead of correcting later, and ask for help before problems harden into crises. That is how teams stay both high-performing and healthy: they achieve results with people, not at their expense, and move forward together, as One Team.

Uncharted Territory

As I began helping teams understand why psychological safety matters and how to put it into practice, I encountered curiosity, uncertainty, and skepticism. Most teams had either never heard the term or understood it only vaguely, and even fewer knew how to bring it to life. The push-back made me ask a deeper question: Why is improving how people work together so often treated as optional?

What kept drawing me back was the idea that how people experience work matters just as much as the work itself. When teams create healthier experiences for people, they also create better conditions for coordination, learning, and performance. I have been part of the Lean Construction community for over a decade, and during this time, I have witnessed tremendous dedication to improving processes to deliver better outcomes. A common saying in this community goes, "Do not blame the people, fix the process." I could not agree more. Yes, blaming people will not do us any good, and yes, processes matter—but I have come to believe that we have focused so heavily on improving processes that we have lost sight of the people making it all happen.

It is people—not processes—who spark improvement, bring engagement to life, and ultimately shape culture. This book is about people—the individuals whose actions and relationships turn good intentions into lasting impact. My dear friend, Paz, who contributed to the final chapter of this book, shared a perspective that has stayed with me:

> *"Sulyn, tú estás quebrando huevos. Para hacer tortillas hay que romper algunos huevos"*
> (Sulyn, you are breaking eggs here. You cannot make omelets without breaking some eggs)

I'm sharing this with you now so you can carry it too, keep it close when you face resistance, and remember that some discomfort is part of meaningful change. I was bringing conversations about psychological safety and behavioral dynamics into construction—a deeply traditional industry shaped by physical labor and historically male-dominated norms. In doing so, I realized that I was not just talking about psychological safety; I was challenging long-standing paradigms:

- The belief that people in this industry do not talk about "stuff" like this.
- The belief that asking for help is a sign of weakness.
- The ideal of toughness that persists in historically male-dominated fields.
- The "I have been doing it this way for 20+ years" mindset.
- The stigma around mental health and a lack of attention to how people feel.
- The normalization of high stress or rude behaviors as "just part of the job."

For me, exploring psychological safety and the behavioral dynamics of teams meant navigating uncharted territory, and it may feel that way for you, too. I'm still learning every day—with every team I meet, every story I hear, and every conversation I have. Yes, the path is not easy, but the discoveries and transformations that await are worth every step into the unknown. This exploration is what led me to the concept of One Team.

One Team

One Team is not just about working well together; it is about working as one. It is a place where authenticity is safe, successes are shared and celebrated, failures are worked through together, and results are owned by the team. You see it when teams show up for one another, build together, and move as one.

One Team emerges when psychological safety and healthy team behaviors come together to create unity, trust, and shared purpose. It is through everyday interactions—speaking up, listening actively, showing respect, caring for others, and learning openly—that this unity takes shape. These behaviors build the relational fabric that holds a team together, helping people navigate pressure, uncertainty, and change.

- One Team means working as one—with care for one another and responsibility for the whole. It means understanding that "my work" and "your work" are connected—and that neither of us can succeed for long at the other's expense.
- It is how healthy teams hold each other accountable without fear—addressing what needs to change while preserving dignity, trust, and belonging.
- It is how high-performing teams operate: When people feel safe and connected, they are more likely to challenge each other constructively, push boundaries, and hold themselves to higher standards—not because they have to but because they want to. These teams excel not just because of individual talent but because they transform individual strengths into collective capability.
- It is how we bring out the best in each other.

Figure 1 represents the synergy that creates One Team: Mindset shapes how we think about one another and the work. Practice shapes how we behave in real moments—how we speak, listen, plan, and respond. Team culture sustains those behaviors over time, reinforcing what is valued and repeated. At the center—where all three dimensions overlap—lies One Team in action: the lived expression of unity that emerges when belief, behavior, and environment move in alignment.

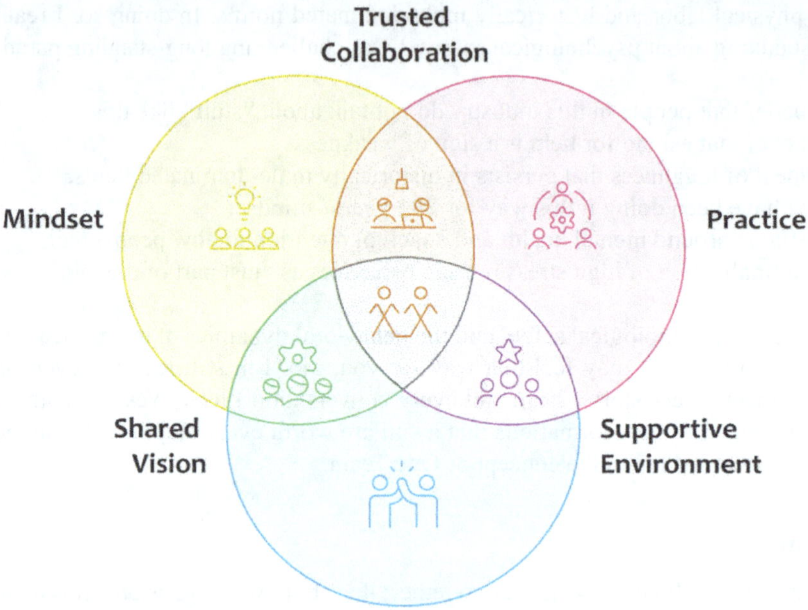

Figure 1 The Synergy of One Team.

This book is an invitation to *build One Team with intention.* Remember *healthy, high-performing teams do not emerge by accident. They are built deliberately*—through everyday behaviors that strengthen trust, improve coordination, and help people bring out the best in one another. No matter where your team begins, I hope these pages inspire you to take the next step toward a stronger, healthier way of working together. Becoming One Team is not a finish line. It is an ongoing practice of courage, care, learning, shared responsibility, and growth.

One last thing before you begin: this book is rich with personal stories. Throughout its pages, you will see photos from different moments in my life to help you spot the stories that come from my own experience. This photo was taken as Glenn and I celebrated my graduation. Glenn was one of my dissertation advisors, and today he is my co-author. It feels fitting to include this photo here because this book grew from the learning, research, and conversations we have shared over the years.

Enjoy!

Introduction

We wrote this book to equip anyone, regardless of role, to guide their team on the journey toward becoming One Team. Although that guidance can come from anyone on the team, formal team leaders play a critical role in enabling psychological safety and modeling the behaviors that hold One Team together. Their openness, responsiveness, and willingness to model vulnerability create the conditions for others to contribute authentically. Without this kind of support, team members may follow the cues they see, hesitate to speak up, or disengage entirely.

That said, building One Team does not depend on leaders alone. This way of operating as One is built through the consistent, intentional behaviors of all team members. When these behaviors align around a shared way of working—with support and example from leadership—they shape how people feel, how they interact, and ultimately, how the team performs. It is this shared responsibility, anchored by strong leadership, that sustains a One Team mindset.

What Do We Mean by "Team"?

We use "team" to talk about a group of people working toward a *common goal*. While some people might use the terms "team" and "group" interchangeably, we treat them as two related but distinct concepts. While both teams and groups involve people coming together, we distinguish them by the degree of interdependence required to achieve a shared outcome. In a team, individuals may carry out tasks independently, but the overarching common goal is only achieved when all the parts can be harmoniously integrated. In groups, however, people may share a common working space or function, but their work is largely self-contained and does not require ongoing coordination with others to be successful.

The construction industry provides clear examples of complex teams. Construction project teams typically have a wide range of members, from the owner of the building to the general contractor and subcontractors building the project, the architects and engineers designing it, and the craftworkers installing the work in place. All these individuals come together, as a team, with one goal: to build a project. Within this large project team, multiple smaller teams emerge. Some focus on structure, others on finishes; some manage design coordination, others field execution. And individuals often belong to several of these teams simultaneously.

This book is written for all teams whose success depends on people working together and relying on one another to accomplish shared outcomes. Whether your team's complexity resembles that of a construction project or takes a simpler form, our belief is the same: every team deserves to work in an environment that fosters psychological safety, where everyone can contribute their unique perspective toward the collective goal of becoming One Team.

Why Begin With Psychological Safety?

Our journey to explore psychological safety started in the Construction Safety Research Group, led by Glenn. Formed in 2016, its goal was to improve safety in construction projects. Despite decades of progress in regulations and policies to keep people safe, data still tells a sobering story. According to the U.S. Bureau of Labor Statistics and the Centers for Disease Control and Prevention, construction remains among the industries with the highest rates of occupational injuries, fatalities, and suicides.[1] These patterns remind us that safety in construction cannot be understood only as compliance with rules or prevention of visible incidents; it must also include the social and psychological conditions of work.

It was this broader view of safety that led us to psychological safety. As we looked for more human-centered ways to understand and address the challenges facing construction teams, psychological safety emerged as a critical area of focus. There was already strong evidence from other industries showing its value for learning, team performance, and speaking up, yet in construction it was still a relatively unfamiliar concept. We began with curiosity, but over time that curiosity turned into conviction. The more we learned, the more clearly we saw that psychological safety is foundational to healthy team dynamics—essential not only to helping teams perform at their best but also to helping the people within them thrive.

We do not claim that other industries have mastered it—far from it. The lessons in this book apply broadly, regardless of the field or team structure. Creating psychological safety and fostering strong team behaviors require deliberate, sustained effort.

Through our work with many teams, we began to notice patterns:

- Some teams naturally fostered psychological safety, even without labeling it as such.
- Others understood its importance but did not know where to begin cultivating it.
- Still others believed they already had it—mistaking the absence of conflict for the presence of safety. We call this a "fake" sense of psychological safety.

We invite you to read this book with a willingness to challenge your assumptions and recognize that psychological safety must be built, sustained, and lived—day by day, behavior by behavior—by every person who aspires to be part of One Team.

In our research, we found that when people feel psychologically safe, they engage more deeply in every aspect of their work. Some of the benefits we observed include:

At the Team Level

- Leveraging diverse perspectives to solve problems collaboratively and creatively.
- Engaging team members in planning their work, creating alignment, and sharing ownership of the plan.
- Fostering transparency and reducing misunderstandings through honest dialogue.
- Learning faster by surfacing plan deviations early—turning mistakes into learning opportunities, not blame, and then turning these opportunities into improvements.
- Enhancing overall performance through knowledge sharing, innovation, and a healthier work-life balance.
- Attracting and retaining talent by cultivating belonging and satisfaction.

At the Individual Level

- Feeling safe speaking up with questions, concerns, or ideas.
- Learning from and with one another, drawing on collective experience.
- Nurturing curiosity and openness to experimentation.
- Contributing while growing personally and professionally.
- Adapting confidently to change.
- Protecting and strengthening mental and emotional wellbeing.
- Developing authentic, lasting relationships built on trust.
- Engaging in constructive conflict and feedback conversations.

When each person is empowered to show up fully, speak with candor, and learn without fear, teams move faster because people are less busy protecting themselves and more focused on delivering value—together.

How to Use This Book

Chapter 1 lays the foundation for building One Team: Psychological Safety. This chapter is meant to help you notice what often goes unseen in daily work—hesitation, silence, fear, futility, and uneven experiences across the team—so you can start building the awareness and dialogue that real change requires.

Chapters 2 through 6 follow a common theme: each explores one essential behavior that helps teams build and sustain One Team. Read these chapters as both reflection and practice. Each one helps you understand why the behavior matters, what it looks like in a team's day-to-day work, and how to begin strengthening it through small, repeatable actions. The "Behavior in Action" sections in these first chapters are your action menu. Use them to move from intention to action. You do not need to do everything at once. Pick a few moves that fit your team and context, try them, and adjust as you learn. As you test these actions, remember that you are not aiming for change overnight; you are building muscle. At the end of each week, ask a simple question: "Where did these behaviors show up this week—and where could we have practiced them more intentionally?" Over time, the actions in this menu will feel less like add-ons and more like part of how your team works.

Chapter 7 is where the book comes together. Read it as the bridge from understanding these behaviors one by one to applying them as a team in real work. This chapter helps you move from reflection to transformation: preparing the ground, choosing where to begin, turning insight into action, and designing conversations and practices that fit your team's reality. This chapter shows that building One Team is not an isolated, one-time event but an ongoing way of working that changes how people relate, align, and perform together.

Chapter 8 invites you to examine these ideas through the lens of leadership, using real examples to show how leaders shape the conditions in which One Team grows stronger or begins to erode.

In this book, you will find strategies for building One Team by cultivating psychological safety and the behaviors that sustain it. You will also read about the struggles we faced while bringing these topics to real team conversations—and the lessons we learned along the way. By sharing both the successes and the challenges, we aim to give you an honest and complete picture of this journey, and to prepare you for your own.

Throughout the book, you will also find facilitator notes, practical tips, and ready-to-use scripts woven into the sections. These are designed to help you lead conversations confidently and safely. We include suggested language to open difficult topics, normalize vulnerability, close the loop, and respond to resistance—because how you frame the conversation can influence whether people lean in or hold back. If you are guiding your team through these discussions, treat these scripts as starting points, adapt them to your voice and context so it can reach your team.

As you read, remember: One Team is built with intention—deliberately, patiently, consistently, and together.

Note

1 For recent national data, see the U.S. Bureau of Labor Statistics, *Census of Fatal Occupational Injuries Report*, and the Centers for Disease Control and Prevention, *Suicide Rates by Industry and Occupation—National Vital Statistics System*, United States. Both sources show that construction continues to face unusually high human risk.

Chapter 1

Diving into Psychological Safety as a Team

Healthy teams shorten the distance between noticing a risk and naming it, between needing help and asking for it, between having an idea and sharing it. Psychological safety is what makes those moves possible.

It Happens With Leadership Too

When I was conducting my doctoral research, I was invited to talk about psychological safety at a meeting of foremen[1]—the frontline leaders who connect decisions made in offices with the daily realities of the field. What I expected to be a simple introduction became a turning point—because it challenged a belief that many of us quietly carry: that leaders "have" psychological safety. That day, I learned something I now repeat often: psychological safety does not come automatically with a role, seniority, or years of experience. It is built through interactions—moment by moment.

In this meeting, I started by explaining the concept of psychological safety to a room full of tough, "macho[2]" men who had been in the trades for decades. My only aim back then was to create awareness and help people see why fostering psychological safety within their teams mattered. Before this meeting, I had heard people from this contractor say things like "everyone here feels safe to speak up" or "we need to drop the term psychologically safe, that is our normal work behavior."

Those comments stayed with me. I understood that for many, the culture was not toxic or harmful, that people were treated reasonably well, and that speaking up was assumed to be part of how the team already worked. From research, I learned that assumptions like these can be misleading. Silence can look like agreement, and compliance can look like commitment.

To explore that further, I used a quick assessment by drawing a 1–7 scale on a board, with one end representing a low psychological safety environment and the other representing a high one. Then I described what each end can look like in practice—whether people ask questions, admit mistakes, raise concerns, and challenge plans early, or whether they stay quiet and play it safe.

DOI: 10.1201/9781003734864-1

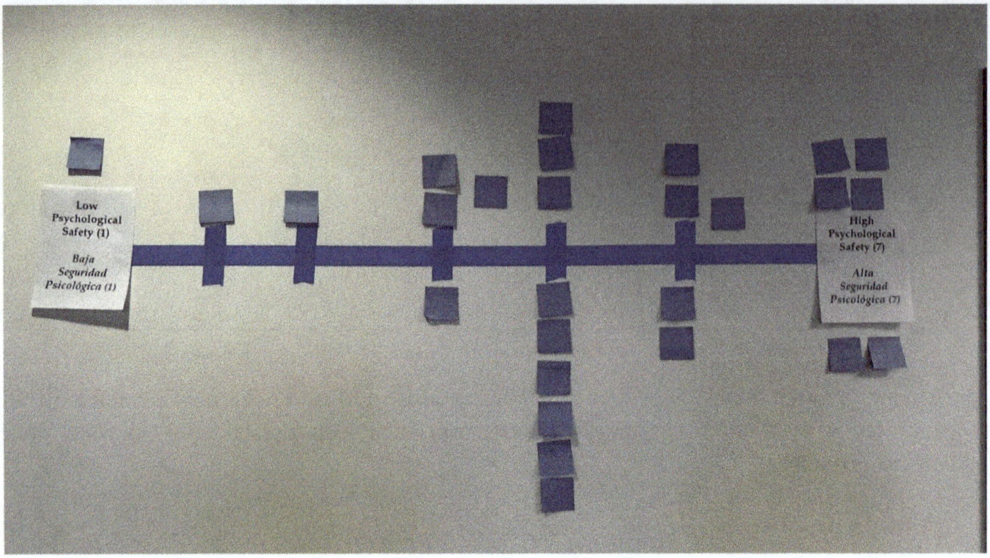

Figure 2 Foremen's Responses to a 1–7 Psychological Safety Exercise.

I asked each foreman to write on a sticky note the number that best reflected how safe they felt speaking up within their teams. When I introduced the exercise, I expected everyone to place themselves at a 6 or 7—after all, this was a leadership group. And to be fair, that expectation was not only mine; it matched what I had been hearing from many in the company.

Then I collected all the sticky notes and placed them on the wall—and the spread across the scale told a different story than the one we were all expecting. The responses were not clustered at the high end. They were scattered (Figure 2). You could see it immediately: some people felt safe to speak, and some were holding back. A few sticky notes landed closer to the lower end of the scale—quiet signals that even in a room full of leaders, some people did not feel safe to speak up and contribute. And those lower ratings carried meaning beyond the numbers themselves. It likely took courage for some participants to choose a 1, 2, or 3, especially in a culture where leaders are often expected to appear tough, capable, and in control. When psychological safety is fragile, people may protect themselves by choosing the answer that feels safer to reveal rather than the one that fully reflects their experience.

The sticky notes had made the invisible visible. What appeared on that wall challenged the assumption that leaders, by virtue of their position, somehow feel safer to speak than everyone else. The uneven spread revealed something more complex: hesitation, variation, and humanity. That was my *aha moment*: psychological safety is not something people automatically gain as they move up. Leaders need it too.

The room seemed to take in that realization with me. I was doing an internship at this company, and my coach attended the meeting with me. When he saw the board, he said out loud what many were thinking: he did not expect the distribution in a room full of leaders to look like that. That simple acknowledgment mattered.

Yes—contrary to popular belief, foremen in construction projects—those strong leaders who guide dozens of craftworkers—can also hesitate to speak up, ask questions, raise concerns, or admit mistakes out loud. The board revealed a simple truth: experience does not erase social risk. We were not talking about psychological safety as an abstract concept anymore—we were looking at it in real time. Even seasoned professionals do quick calculations about how their words will land and what it might cost them. We learned then: *real leadership is not the absence of fear. It is the ability to notice where fear is shaping behavior—and to deliberately lower the cost of honesty for others, and for yourself.*

Until then, psychological safety had been, in some ways, taken for granted. But the board exposed a gap between assumption and reality. People had been saying that speaking up was simply part of the culture; the responses showed that this was not true for everyone. Once that gap became visible, the conversation changed. We were no longer talking about whether psychological safety mattered. We were confronting where it was present and where it was fragile. That shift became a turning point in my doctoral research and in how this team began to think about psychological safety—not as a label to defend but as a reality to understand and improve together.

In that moment, the team was beginning to practice what it means to become One Team. This begins when people are willing to see reality together, take responsibility for it together, and care for one another in the process. It is the feeling that we belong to the same "we": that your problem is my problem, raising your concern protects all of us, and your question is welcome because it helps us do better. When teams are healthy, people do not have to "gear up" to speak—they speak because they trust the relationship underneath the work. Being One Team means we make space for each other every day: we notice who is quiet, we invite the voices closest to the work, we respond with respect, and we follow through so people learn that their voice matters. That sense of being in it together is what makes speaking up feel natural, not risky.

From that day forward, I stopped assuming safety and started observing and influencing behaviors. This book is intended to equip you to do the same with your team. Whatever your role, this chapter shares the core insights we gained while facilitating real conversations about psychological safety—one of the core conditions that enable teams to work as one.

The sections to follow are meant to offer moments to pause, reflect, begin these conversations, and connect with your team in new ways. Psychological safety often begins with awareness, but it deepens through dialogue. That dialogue is rarely straightforward. It requires us to look beneath the surface—past assumptions, past titles, past routines, and the "we have always done it this way" mentality—and pay attention to the hesitation before someone speaks, the courage it takes to ask a question, and the care we show when someone opens up. Together, we will explore something that often goes unseen—silence. We begin by examining silence as both a signal that deeper conversation is needed and an opportunity for the team to explore how to make it safer—for everyone—to speak up. You will notice that you do not need to have all the answers. You just need to be willing to start the conversation—and keep returning to it, little by little, as your team learns to notice more, name more, and respond in ways that make speaking up feel safer over time.

1.1 Looking into Silence: Fear and Futility

When we talk about psychological safety, we often focus on what people say: on their ideas, questions, concerns, or feedback. But just as important, and sometimes more revealing, is what people do not say. Silence in teams is often mistakenly interpreted as agreement or neutrality. More often, silence is a signal, one that points to something deeper and stems from two invisible but powerful forces: fear and futility.[3]

Fear[4] shows up when individuals anticipate that speaking up will lead to negative consequences such as being judged, reprimanded, dismissed, or excluded. This fear can stem from past experiences, perceived hierarchies, or team norms in which mistakes are punished, and questions are seen as weaknesses. People may fear being seen as difficult or incompetent. They might stay silent to avoid conflict or embarrassment—even when they have valuable insights that could help the team. Even subtle signals, like eye-rolls or interruptions, can reinforce this fear and silence voices before they are ever heard. In these situations, silence is a self-protective response, rooted in a lack of psychological safety.

Futility,[5] on the other hand, is rooted in the belief that speaking up will not make a difference. People experiencing futility are not necessarily afraid; they are convinced that nothing will change. They have spoken up in the past and been ignored. Or they have seen others raise concerns that went nowhere. When people feel that their input does not matter and that their voice will be dismissed, they may stop speaking up altogether.

Fear asks, "What will this cost me?" Futility asks, "What good will it do?" Both keep teams quiet when candor and kindness would be of most help.

Fear and futility are two of the greatest barriers to people speaking up, and perhaps most concerningly, they often go unnoticed. Silence is easy to overlook. It is invisible. It does not interrupt a meeting or raise red flags. It quietly corrodes performance and connection from the inside. When silence becomes the default strategy, teams may look calm on the surface while issues accumulate underneath: feedback loops break down or are nonexistent, learning stalls, and small issues grow into large ones. Treat silence like smoke: not proof of fire but a reason to check the room. Over time, this erodes trust and fragments the sense of unity that characterizes a healthy team.

As we worked with team members across different roles, we began to see patterns in how fear and futility showed up. When asked if they had ever remained silent even though they had something to say that could benefit their teams, nearly all participants said yes. But the reasons varied. Some described moments when they feared judgment or backlash from their leaders or peers. Others shared stories of offering ideas in the past that were ignored, dismissed, never acknowledged, or followed by no visible action. Both experiences led them to conclude that speaking up was not worth it or that it was not worth the risk. Most often, people are not deciding whether they have something to contribute, but whether the environment can handle the contribution. Figure 3 illustrates the responses of a couple of these teams.

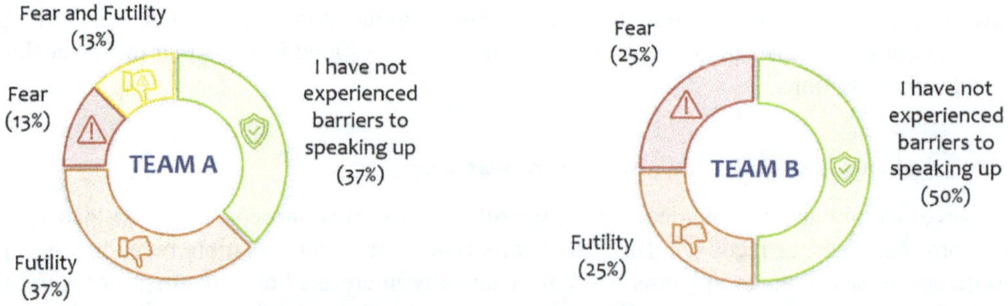

Figure 3 Fear and Futility in Sample Teams.

Start looking at silence as a symptom that points to a dynamic below the surface. If we are truly committed to cultivating One Team, we cannot just listen to the loudest voices. We have to notice who is not speaking. We have to ask why. And we have to make it safe—and worth it—for everyone to be heard.

The presence of silence does not always mean there is a problem, but it always deserves exploration.[6] Are people quiet because they agree, or because they have given up? Are they quiet because they are reflecting or because they do not feel it is safe to speak? These are the kinds of questions leaders and team members alike must learn to ask.

In one of our talks at the 2025 Lean Construction Institute (LCI) Congress, we asked attendees, "What gets in your way of speaking up?" This congress typically brings together experienced Lean practitioners—including project executives, project managers, superintendents, trade partners, designers, and owners' representatives—people who are actively working to improve project delivery and team performance in real-world settings. In other words, this was not a room of people unfamiliar with collaboration, reflection, or continuous improvement. And still, when we asked what gets in the way of speaking up, the responses were immediate and deeply human. We collected 65 responses, presented in participants' own words in Figure 4. When we grouped those responses into themes, a clear pattern emerged (Figure 5). The most prominent barrier was fear—mostly fear of social evaluation (embarrassment, judgment, rejection), with some concerns about punishment or retaliation. Futility appeared next—people worried that nothing would happen or that their ideas would be dismissed. Inclusion barriers reflected language and cultural gaps. The rest clustered around other themes such as process, power dynamics, and experience. Taken together, these responses remind us that even among seasoned professionals, speaking up can still feel risky.

Becoming One Team means doing more than inviting people to speak; it means creating conditions that make speaking feel safer and more worthwhile. It means responding to fear with empathy and replacing futility with visible follow-through. Only when people believe that their voice will be heard and that their words will lead to meaningful conversation or change can teams move from a collection of individuals to becoming One Team, working toward a shared purpose.

Figure 4 Barriers to Speaking Up Word Cloud, LCI 2025 Congress.

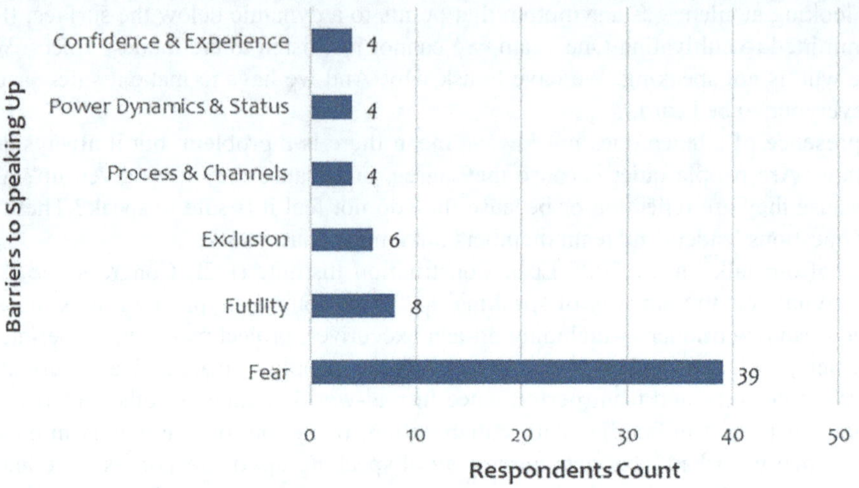

Figure 5 Themes of Barriers to Speaking Up, LCI 2025 Congress.

We have to look beneath silence and be brave enough to break it.

> **Team Commitment**
>
> Pick one meeting this week and explicitly thank the first three people who raise risks or questions. Make a point of inviting—and acknowledging—a contribution from someone who speaks less often.

Silence, fear, and futility do not show up randomly. They are shaped by the conditions teams operate in every day—what is expected, what is rewarded, and what quietly goes unquestioned. If psychological safety feels fragile, the issue is rarely a lack of care or awareness. More often, the environment is built on the assumption that speaking up will just happen.

1.2 Setting the Stage

Start by discussing a common expectation we often hear in the workplace:

"If they have a question, they need to let me know."

On the surface, this might sound reasonable. But this expectation rests on a hidden assumption—that people, for the most part, feel psychologically safe to speak up. And that is a dangerous assumption. While some people may feel confident asking questions or raising concerns, others may not. They might hesitate, not because they do not care, but because they are unsure how their input will be received.

Let's say you ask someone to complete a task. If the person does not feel safe enough to ask clarifying questions, they may walk away with incomplete information, and the result may fall short of what was needed. Here are a few questions someone might have wanted to ask but did not:

> "Can you please clarify what you mean by . . ."
>
> "Is there anything I should avoid or be especially careful about?"
>
> "Who should I involve or check with before moving forward?"

Expectation clarity is a system property, not a personal virtue. If people are not asking, assume the environment—not the individual—needs attention. Healthy teams do not rely on mind-reading; they build routines that make questions normal. Reframe the expectation:

> "If they have a question and does not ask it, we need to understand what got in the way and address it together."

If we only reward people for being fast, quiet, and compliant—then "no questions" becomes the behavior that gets reinforced. This reframing shifts some of the responsibility back to the team and the environment it creates. It asks us to consider: Are we creating an environment where people truly feel safe to speak up? Are we taking action when they do? Or are we unknowingly reinforcing silence?

Mini Practice (5 Minutes)

End one meeting this week by asking, "What is one instruction we could clarify right now?" Capture it. Clarify it. Close the loop in the next meeting.

Facilitator/Leader Script

"If something is unclear to you, it is likely unclear to someone else too—thank you for raising it."

As you set the stage to have these conversations with your team, remember that perception and reality are not always aligned. Some people may believe that their team is open, while others in the same team may still be hesitating or staying quiet. Without checking where people actually stand, even well-intended actions can miss the mark or reinforce silence. And often, the clearest cost of that silence is not visible in the moment—it lives in the missed opportunities: the questions not asked, the ideas not shared, and the concerns raised too late.

1.3 Highlighting Missed Opportunities

One activity we often use with teams is designed to surface what we call missed opportunities. These are the moments when someone had something valuable to say but stayed silent. At first, people may assume this does not happen often. Some team members may even believe that as long as the team is not in crisis or no one is quitting, everything must be fine, and psychological safety must be strong.

But we encourage you to look deeper. Ask yourself this question: Have you ever had a question or idea but stayed quiet because no one else was speaking up either?

Every time someone holds back, the team misses an opportunity to learn, improve, or prevent a problem. Silence does not just affect the individual, it ripples through the whole team. When silence is normalized, it slowly erodes the potential for growth, collaboration, and innovation.

It also delays the team's ability to respond. In construction projects, this delay can be especially costly. A risk may be noticed early—such as a defect in the field—but if no one speaks up, the team does not hear about it until later, when the consequences are harder to contain.

Asking teams the following question can open the door to a powerful conversation:

> *"When working with your team, have you ever remained silent even though you had something valuable to contribute?"*

Then, invite team members to respond individually. Ask each person to place a check mark on a sticky note if their answer is yes. Once everyone has responded, collect the sticky notes and post them on a wall where the team can observe the overall pattern. Figures 6 and 7 illustrate the responses of two different teams.[7] In one team, 26 out of 28 craftworkers reported remaining silent. In the other, 17 out of 18 staff members said the same.

Figure 6 Craftworker Team Responses on Remaining Silent Question (26/28 yes).

Figure 7 Staff Team Responses on Remaining Silent Question (17/18 yes).

These results are not unusual. We have seen similar patterns across different roles, teams, and industries. Silence is more common than most teams realize, and because it often leaves no immediate trace, it is easy to overlook unless teams intentionally make space to see it. But once they do, something important begins to shift. What was hidden becomes a shared signal—something the team can learn from, respond to, and work to change.

Facilitator Note

Thank your team for participating. Acknowledge that naming silence takes courage and is an act of vulnerability—and that courage and vulnerability deserve care. These conversations create an opportunity for people to be honest about their experiences. That honesty can become the starting point for learning, action, and growth.

Micro-commitments

Turn what surfaced in the conversation into small, visible actions the team can practice consistently. For example:

- Make "One risk we are not saying out loud yet" a standing agenda item.
- Run a 10-minute pre-mortem before milestones: "Imagine this failed—what likely caused it?"
- Add a "good catch" line in recaps (name who surfaced a risk).

When teams see how common silence really is, the conversation naturally deepens. The question becomes less about whether people stay quiet and more about what is making silence feel safer than speaking. Silence is not accidental; it is often learned, reinforced, and shaped over time. To change what shows up in the room, teams need to understand what sits beneath the surface of behavior.

1.4 Navigating the Roots

To shift a team's dynamics—the everyday ways people work together—and become One Team, we first need to understand what shapes those dynamics. Psychological safety is not a nice-to-have feeling; it is a practical condition that shapes whether truth travels fast or gets stuck. This section helps teams navigate the roots of psychological safety and the behaviors that support or undermine it. We ground the concept in research, then connect it to lived experience—because teams do not change through definitions alone; they change when they recognize themselves in the patterns.

Psychological Safety

When introducing psychological safety to your team, make the concept clear, relevant, and connected to everyday work. Explain what it means at its core, how our understanding of it has evolved over time, and why it matters to the team's ability to work and succeed as one.

The idea of psychological safety did not arrive fully formed as we understand it today—it has been refined over decades of research.[8] What began as a concept tied to how people navigated change evolved into a broader workplace experience: being able to show up, contribute, and stay engaged

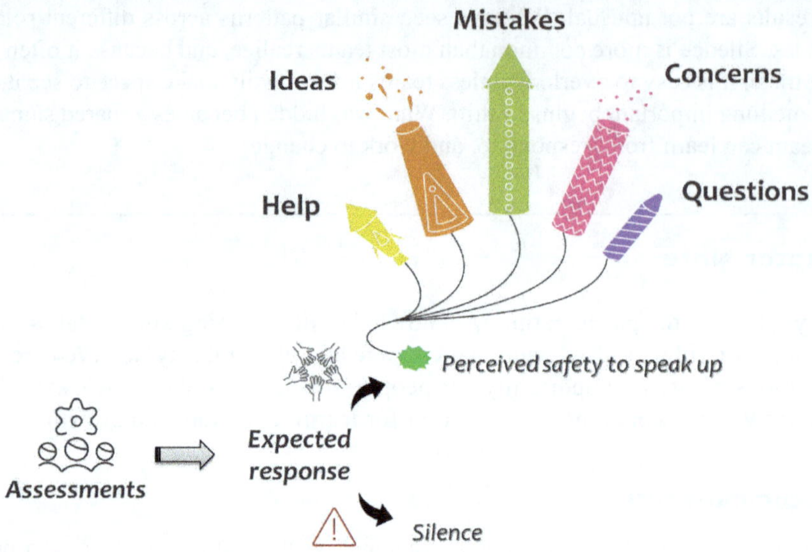

Figure 8 Psychological Safety in Action.

without fear of social or professional consequences. Today, we most often use it at the team level because it is created (or eroded) in interaction with others. It shows up in the micro-moments that follow voice: what happens after a question, after a concern, after a mistake, after a dissenting view.

Figure 8 illustrates how psychological safety operates in real time. Before anyone speaks up with an idea, question, concern, mistake, or request for help, something happens internally. People make quick assessments about the expected response. These assessments occur almost instantly, often shaped by prior experiences, team norms, power dynamics, and observed reactions to others who have spoken up.

If the expected response is curious, respectful, and solution-oriented, people perceive greater psychological safety. When perceived safety is high, voice behaviors are more likely to occur. Ideas are shared. Mistakes are admitted earlier. Concerns surface before they escalate. Questions are asked while there is still time to adjust. Requests for help happen before rework is required.

If the expected response is punitive, dismissive, or unpredictable, perceived safety drops. Behavior changes accordingly. Ideas are filtered. Concerns are softened. Mistakes are hidden. Silence replaces contribution. What could have helped the team move forward gets delayed, diluted, or lost altogether.

Psychological safety is the social permission people feel to bring the best version of themselves into the work. This is what creates fertile ground for One Team to grow. Without psychological safety, collaboration is shallow, trust is fragile, and feedback loops are broken. With psychological safety, people align not just on tasks but on purpose. Truth shows up earlier, learning travels faster, and problems get solved with the team—rather than around the team.

Behaviors

We understand *behaviors* simply as what people do—how they act, react, speak, and listen. Most often, the behaviors people bring to work every day are often rooted in past experiences. Behaviors are the visible layer; underneath them are beliefs, experiences, and expectations about what is safe and what is worth it. For example, someone who was ridiculed in a previous job for asking a question, or who got in trouble for pointing out a mistake, may now choose to stay silent. Another person might avoid offering ideas if they had felt that their ideas were dismissed or ignored before.

The good news: Behaviors are malleable. And often, what it takes to change them is a trigger, an experience that prompts people to reflect and act. We hope this book becomes that trigger for your team, not by pushing people to "be braver" but by helping teams redesign the conditions that make speaking up normal.

As you explore the dynamics of your team, we invite you to look not only at what people are doing but also at why. What might be behind a teammate's silence? What past experience could be shaping someone's reluctance to ask questions? What have they learned will happen if they raise a risk? These are the invisible roots beneath the surface-level behaviors. By bringing these roots into the open, teams can begin to shift their habits in ways that build connection, trust, and shared ownership.

Explore Perspectives

When introducing psychological safety to your team, you can start by inviting them into the definition—before you offer one. Ask a simple opener: "What does psychological safety mean to you?" You are not looking for the "right" definition—you are trying to understand how your team currently makes sense of the idea.

We often hear a wide range of responses—especially when the term is new to the team. We have seen some people describe psychological safety as the absence of fear. Others name respect, support, or being able to speak freely. Others simply say, "I'm not sure." Taken together, these responses give you a starting point to begin your conversation.

In a session with the Lean[9] Construction Institute's Northern California Community of Practice, we asked this question. Figure 9 illustrates some of the responses we received, ranging from "positive financial prospect" to "no idea is too silly to share" to "huh?" (i.e., "I have no idea").

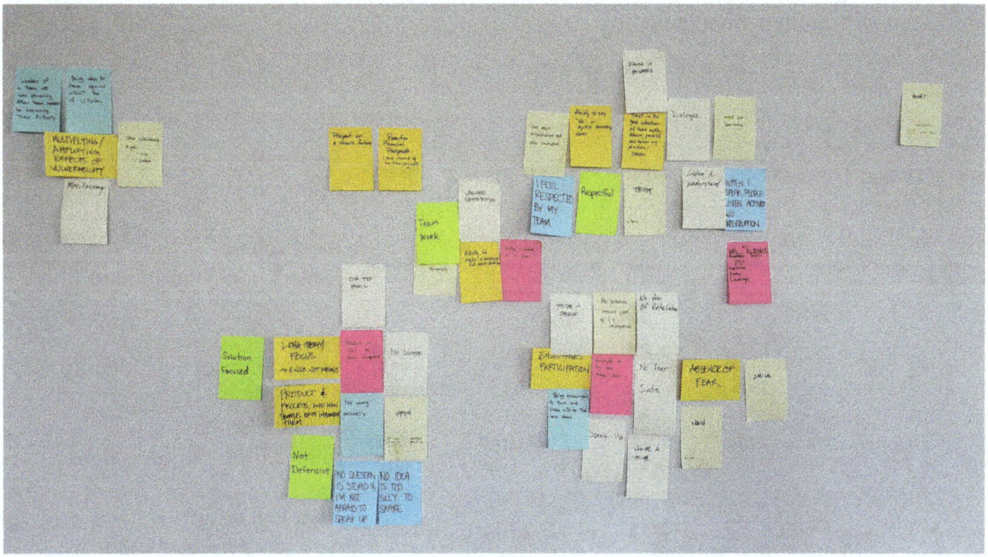

Figure 9 Lean Team Responses to Question "What Is Psychological Safety to You?"

These responses show why teams should not assume that everyone understands or experiences psychological safety in the same way. Rather than trying to force a single definition, teams can use these differences as a starting point for building a shared understanding of how they want to work together. By openly defining what respectful collaboration looks like, how they want to give and receive feedback, and how they respond when someone makes a mistake, they move from individual guesswork to collective clarity. The goal is to make psychological safety visible and actionable by clarifying what it should look and feel like in the team's daily interactions.

As you explore different perspectives, remember what we referred to as a "fake" sense of psychological safety in the book introduction. In our work with leaders, we often see this misconception. Teams assume everything is fine because no one is complaining, quitting, or openly clashing. But the absence of visible conflict is not the same as safety. Just because things are not bad, it does not mean they cannot be better. And "good enough" is not the same as healthy. Some of the strongest teams we have worked with were already performing well. What helped them grow stronger was their willingness to examine how they worked together—and their courage to adjust behaviors that quietly limited learning and voice.

Figure 10 makes the distinction between a fake and a real sense of psychological safety visible. Statements such as "There's no conflict" or "My door is always open" may express good intentions, but they do not necessarily tell us whether people experience safety, voice, care, inclusion, and learning in practice. Use the figure to help your team look beyond what is said and examine what people actually experience. Ask: Which of these phrases do we rely on? What would these deeper conditions look like in our everyday interactions?

Making these behaviors visible and discussable helps teams turn psychological safety from a vague aspiration to an intentional, shared practice. When teams consistently practice behaviors that signal respect, curiosity, and follow-through, people begin to engage differently. They speak sooner. They listen more openly. They take responsibility together.

Once teams have begun to understand psychological safety—what it is, what shapes it, and how it shows up in behavior—the next step is to examine how safe it currently feels for people to speak up within their own team.

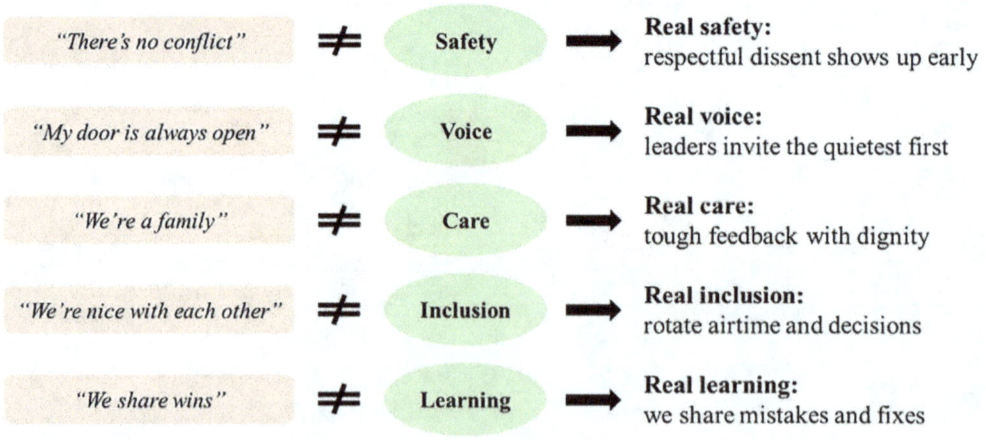

Figure 10 Fake Versus Real Psychological Safety Signals.

1.5 Assessing Where Your Team Stands

Psychological safety can be misread—especially when a few confident voices dominate the room. To move beyond surface impressions, teams need a shared snapshot: a way to see how safe it actually feels to speak up today. Too often, teams move too quickly from intention to action without first understanding where they are starting from and what may need attention. Assessment, when done well, is not about labeling teams as good or bad; it is about creating a common reference point for learning. You can use any tool that feels appropriate for your context. What matters most is creating spaces for people to reflect and speak honestly. In our work, we often rely on:

1. The One Team Dynamics assessment,[10] which measures team behavioral dynamics and psychological safety
2. Variations of Amy Edmondson's original psychological safety survey[11]

The One Team Dynamics assessment provides an overview of both psychological safety and the key team behavioral dynamics explored more deeply in Chapters 2–6. In doing so, it helps teams understand not only whether people feel safe to speak up but also how everyday behaviors may be supporting—or undermining—healthy teamwork.

Tips for rolling out this assessment:

- Clarify the purpose: Be upfront about why participation matters, what the team hopes to learn, and how the results will be used. Make clear that the assessment is meant to support team learning and improvement—not to evaluate individuals or assign blame.
- Protect the person: Be clear about whether responses will be anonymous or confidential, how anonymity will be protected, who will have access to the data, and how the results will be shared. This helps people respond more honestly, especially those who may feel least safe.
- Use channels that fit your audience: Offer multiple ways to participate and consider access to technology, language needs, privacy, and the time available so everyone has a fair opportunity to respond.
- Co-develop the action plan: Bring the results back to the team, discuss patterns openly, and involve them in deciding what comes next. This reinforces that their voice matters.
- Close the loop visibly: Share a simple "We agreed/We did" update. Implement, report back, adjust, and repeat. This builds trust and reduces futility.

While the assessment approaches described in this section provide valuable insights, they are not always the only—or the fastest—way to begin the conversation. Sometimes teams need a simpler tool that helps people picture what psychological safety looks like in their teams. The psychological safety spectrum in the next section serves that purpose well. It turns an abstract concept into something more concrete, while also giving teams a fast way to surface variation in how safe it feels to speak up.

1.6 Exploring Psychological Safety as a Dynamic Range

One way to make this concept real for teams is to describe what psychological safety sounds like in everyday language:

"I do not know how to do this; could you help me?"
"I made a mistake, let's review this together"

"I have a different idea; can I share it?"
"I may be missing something—can you help me understand?"

These statements are more likely to be heard when the surrounding environment makes it safe—and worthwhile—to speak. To help teams surface and examine these conditions, we often use the psychological safety spectrum (Figure 11) as a conversation tool. The spectrum turns invisible team dynamics into something people can see, discuss, and act on together.

Think of the spectrum as having a 1–7 scale, where 1 represents low psychological safety and 7 represents high psychological safety. A "1" reflects fear, avoidance, or silence. A "7" reflects openness, curiosity, and mutual support. The middle of the spectrum—a "3" to a "5" typically—is where most teams spend most of their time. Here, people are not silent, but they are cautious. Voice is selective. Questions are asked privately. Risks are filtered. Issues surface later than they could. Teams in this range may appear "fine," even though important learning, coordination, and prevention opportunities are being missed.

Figure 11 illustrates how psychological safety shows up behaviorally across the spectrum—from self-protection on the left to contribution on the right. The spectrum is not meant to label people or teams. Its value lies in helping teams read their environment more clearly.

On the low psychological safety end, behaviors tend to center on protection. People may hesitate, stay silent, rely only on themselves, avoid difficult conversations, or conceal concerns and mistakes. These behaviors are often misinterpreted as disengagement or lack of ownership.

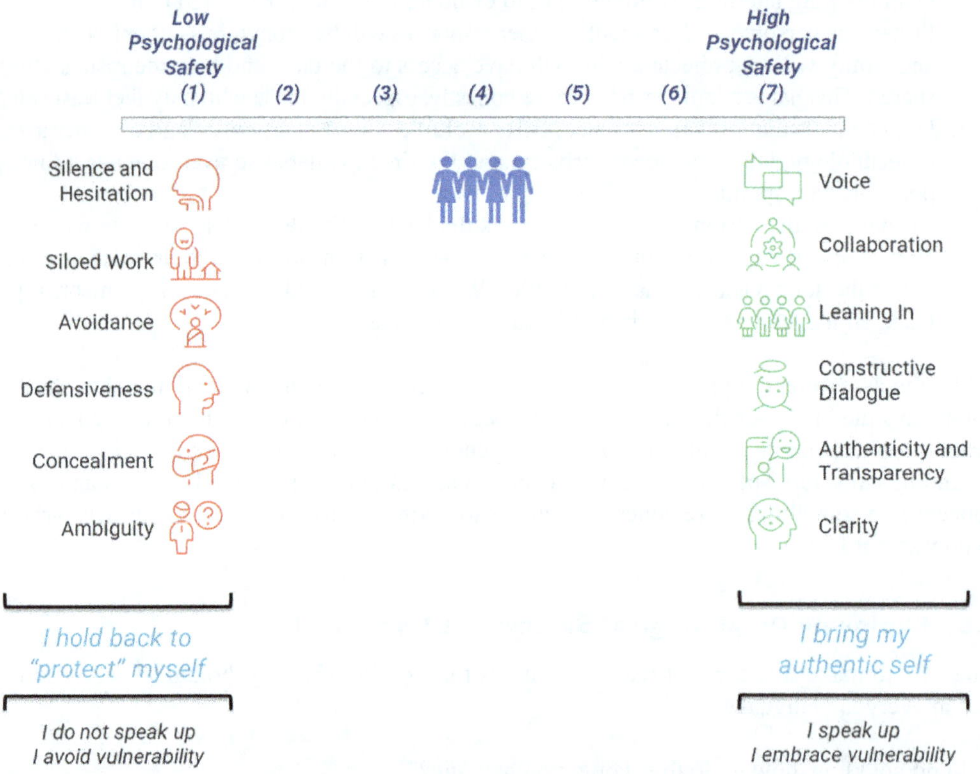

Figure 11 Behaviors in Low and High Psychological Safety Environments.

In reality, they are adaptive responses to perceived risk. People are not withholding because they do not care—they are holding back to protect themselves.

On the high psychological safety end, behaviors shift toward contribution. Open communication, collaboration, proactive problem-solving, constructive disagreement, authenticity, and clarity become more visible. People speak sooner, ask for help earlier, and share incomplete thinking without fear of punishment or embarrassment. Vulnerability becomes a strength rather than a liability. In healthy teams, this is what "high performance" looks like in real time: earlier warnings, cleaner coordination, and faster recovery after mistakes.

The power of the spectrum emerges when teams see how experiences differ across individuals within a team. Psychological safety is rarely evenly distributed. These differences are not personal shortcomings; they are signals about how the environment is working.

Psychological safety is shaped in small, repeatable moments. Each interaction teaches people something about what is safe to say, when to say it, and whether it is worth the risk. Because psychological safety is built incrementally, it can also be strengthened incrementally. A "+1" mindset helps teams focus on the next meaningful improvement rather than aiming for a perfect score. Instead of asking how to get everyone to a 7, ask: What is one change we can make that would move us one step to the right? This keeps the work practical, gives the team something specific to try, and allows trust to grow through visible, repeated actions.

Here are some ways you can facilitate this conversation:

- **Individual Reflection**
  Purpose: Give participants space to reflect privately on how psychologically safe they feel and what experiences have shaped that perception.

Invite each person to review the behaviors at both ends of the spectrum and reflect privately:

"Where would you place your experience of psychological safety on your team today?"

One of the first times I facilitated this reflection, I shared an experience of working with someone I feared. At the time, I would have rated my experience on that team as a 1. As I described the experience, my voice began to break, and I found myself unable to contain my tears. For a moment, the room froze. What followed was empathy. That moment changed the tone of the conversation and opened the space for others to connect and share. People began to reflect on their own experiences—times when they, too, felt hesitant, guarded, or afraid. Sharing that experience opened the door to a broader recognition: fear, self-protection, and uncertainty are not signs of weakness but part of being human. The conversation shifted from guarded to open, and that shift mattered. It reminded us that beneath roles, titles, and professional armor, people carry history, feelings, and the lessons they have learned from past experiences into the work. Once that became visible, the conversation was no longer just about my experience. It became a space for others to make sense of their own—and for the team to reflect together on what they wanted to change and how they wanted to show up differently for one another.

- **Small Group Conversation**
  Purpose: Quick pulse for small teams; a visual, low-friction way to surface variation.

Try this:

1. Ask each person to write a number from 1 to 7 on a sticky note indicating how safe it currently feels to speak up within their team.
2. Collect and post the notes yourself to preserve anonymity, or invite people to post them if the group is ready.
3. Step back and debrief:
   - What patterns do you notice?
   - What would move the team one step to the right in the next few weeks?

This is the strategy I have used the most, especially when a full, in-depth assessment cannot be conducted due to time constraints. This visual tool is a simple but powerful representation of the team as a unit. When I used this strategy in a foremen peer group meeting, the board became a shared picture of the team's experiences. The diversity in these numbers became a catalyst for conversation, as if the act of physically placing their sticky notes on the wall had freed them to explore their feelings and experiences. The transparency of the exercise laid the groundwork for open communication and mutual understanding.

Seeing the range of experiences side by side often creates a powerful realization: we can no longer take psychological safety for granted. Some people speak freely, while others hesitate. When teams notice this variation together, they gain a shared reference point for improvement—one grounded in reality rather than assumption.

What matters most is how the team is willing to respond to what it sees. Small adjustments—how questions are welcomed, how concerns are acknowledged, how follow-through is handled—can meaningfully shift how safe it feels to speak. Over time, these small shifts compound, moving the team toward a stronger One Team.

- **Large Group Conversation**
  Purpose: High-participation pulse for large audiences; it creates a powerful shared picture quickly.

Facilitator Safeguard

Because participants' responses will be visible, remind everyone that participation is voluntary and that they may choose to pass without explanation. Frame the activity as a collective snapshot rather than an evaluation of individual participants, and do not ask anyone to explain or defend their rating. During the debrief, focus on the overall distribution and what it reveals about the range of experiences that can exist.

Try this:

1. Ask everyone to stand (or raise hands, depending on the space)
2. Invite those who feel like a 1 to sit. Pause and let the room take in what they see
3. Repeat for 2, 3, and 4. Often, about half the room is seated by this point
4. Repeat for 5 and 6. Notice how the number standing typically narrows
5. Before calling 7, name the moment: "We have more awareness now. The goal is moving forward together."

The first time I used this strategy was during a talk at the Civil Engineering Students Conference in Peru. My topic, psychological safety, was a bit atypical for engineering students, even more so in Peru. The turnout exceeded my expectations, with over one hundred attendees. When I asked those who felt like a "1" to take a seat, a significant portion of the audience sat. The final call for those identifying as a "7" resonated with only a handful, scattered across the room. It was a powerful moment of realization for the entire audience. The students were seeing themselves in relation to each other, many for the first time. Some looked surprised. Others nodded as if they could finally put a name to something they had felt for a long time. Then I asked what it would take for more of them to feel like a "6" or a "7." One said, "We need to stop laughing when someone asks a question that may seem obvious." Another added, "I think we need to give each other more encouragement, just a little goes a long way." The conversation flowed naturally. And what started as a quiet exercise became a moment of co-creation where the idea of psychological safety became theirs, not just mine.

I used this strategy again at the Lean Construction Congress in Mexico in 2023, with around 300 attendees, most of them seasoned industry professionals. I watched as the room embraced the vulnerability inherent in the exercise. As participants began to take their seats based on their perceived level of psychological safety, the visual representation unfolded before my eyes once again. By the time I called for those who identified as a "7" to take their seats, only a few remained standing. The room fell into a moment of contemplative silence, as the variation in people's experience became visible to everyone at once.

- **Online Format**
  Purpose: Quick pulse for teams that need anonymity, speed, or geographic flexibility.

Try this:

1. Set up a 1–7 scale on your preferred platform[12] and display the live distribution without names so participants can see patterns with less social risk.
2. Add one optional, open-ended prompt, such as: "What is one small change that would make it safer for people on this team to speak up?" to capture concrete, actionable ideas in participants' own words.

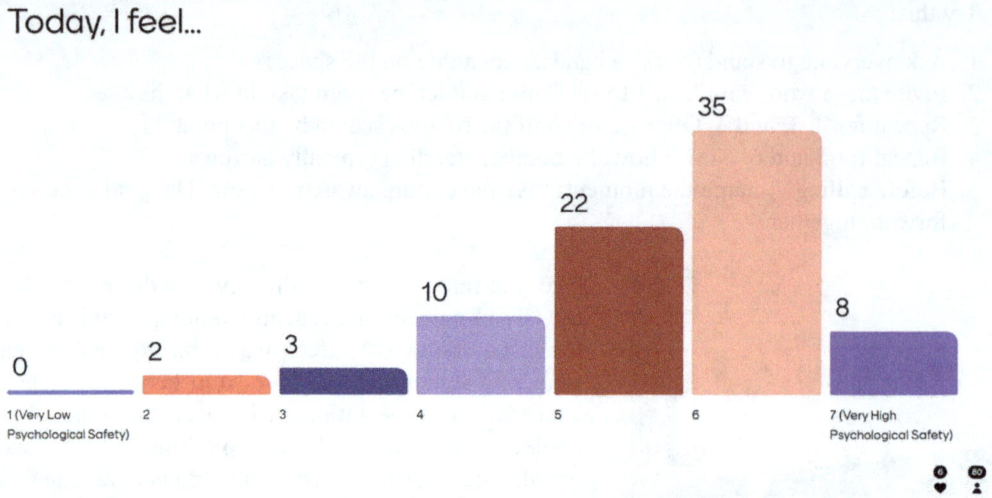

Figure 12 Psychological Safety as Experienced by Superintendents.

> In a peer group meeting with superintendents from a general contractor, the distribution in Figure 12 revealed meaningful variation in how psychological safety was experienced across the group: 54% of participants selected 6 or 7, while 46% selected 5 or below, including 19% at 4 or below. Although the overall distribution leaned toward higher ratings, the spread indicates that psychological safety was not experienced consistently across the group. For nearly half of the participants, speaking up still involved some degree of hesitation, caution, or restraint. Superintendents are senior field leaders who coordinate work, navigate pressure, and influence how openly issues are discussed on a project. Their willingness to raise concerns—and how they respond when others do—help signal to foremen and crews whether speaking up is welcomed and worthwhile. When superintendents themselves hesitate to speak up, others may be even more reluctant to do so.

We have seen similar patterns emerge across settings, from university classrooms to seasoned professionals. When people are given a way to see themselves in relation to others, what begins as an exercise often becomes a collective moment of recognition. Psychological safety is not a given, and it is not owned by any one role. Fostering psychological safety is a shared responsibility.

Our question to you:

> "What is one behavior you will try this week to make it safer for others on your team to speak up?"

1.7 Understanding Nuances Within a Team

Once a team understands what psychological safety is and why it matters, the next step is to recognize how it actually shows up in practice. Psychological safety is not a fixed state you either have or do not have. It is context-dependent, experienced at different levels, and shaped by everyday interactions. Within the same team, it can rise or fall over time—depending on how people respond to one another, especially in moments of uncertainty, disagreement, or conflict. Healthy teams do not pretend this fluctuation is not real—they learn to notice it early and respond.

People do not experience psychological safety in the same way across every relationship. Someone may feel safe speaking up with a peer but hesitate with a supervisor or client. When people describe what they see and feel in their teams, they often speak from their own perspective. A senior manager may say, "I feel safe to speak up," but a frontline worker in the same team may not. Looking at these differences helps teams identify the relationships and situations where people are most likely to hesitate before speaking up—and where the team needs to be more intentional about making voice feel safe and worthwhile.

We saw this pattern clearly in construction project teams. These teams are inherently complex, bringing together people from different organizations—general contractors, trade partners, designers, and owners—each with distinct responsibilities, incentives, and power dynamics. Stakeholder boundaries amplify complexity. In our assessments, people frequently reported higher psychological safety with internal teammates and lower safety with external stakeholders—even though all were part of the same project team (Figures 13 and 14 illustrate the results of two construction teams). Ironically, many of the most critical conversations cross these boundaries—precisely where safety is weakest.

One project manager captured this boundary tension with striking honesty:

> "With my team, I feel safe flagging issues. But when it comes to telling the architect or owner something went wrong. . . . You just can't afford to get it wrong."
>
> Project manager, Team A

That phrase—"You can't afford to get it wrong"—reveals the real-time calculation that people make. It is not only about competence, but also about reputation, financial impact, relational strain, and perceived authority. When that internal calculation tips toward risk, information

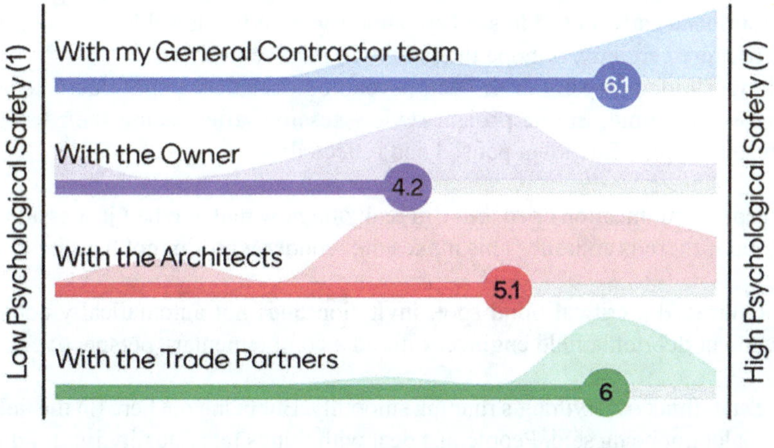

Figure 13 Psychological Safety Assessment From the General Contractor's Perspective (Team A, 12 Participants).

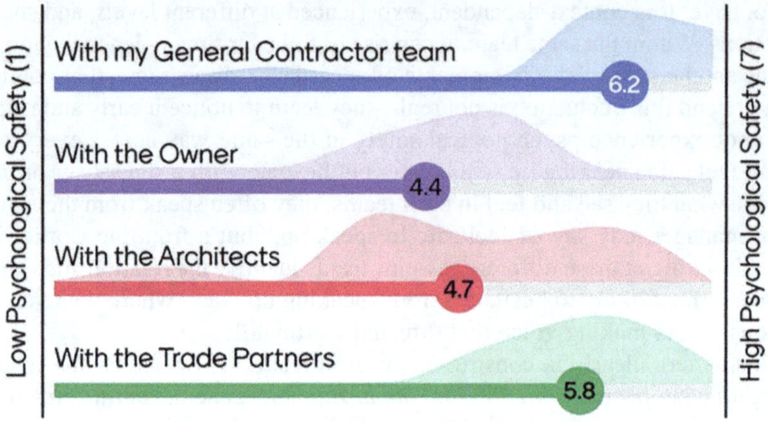

Figure 14 **Psychological Safety Assessment from the General Contractor's Perspective (Team B, 13 Participants).**

slows down. Concerns are softened. Warnings are delayed. And small issues quietly gain momentum before the broader team ever hears about them. This delay is known as latency—the gap between that moment when someone first notices a risk and when the broader team becomes aware of it. In complex projects, that gap is costly. The longer a concern stays localized, the more likely it is to compound—affecting quality, schedule, coordination, and trust. Latency is the hidden tax unhealthy teams pay: not because people do not see problems but because it does not feel safe—or useful—to name them when they see them.

High-stakes boundary conversations—such as discussing scope gaps, change orders, or unexpected delays—are precisely where latency tends to increase. These moments carry financial, contractual, and reputational implications. When psychological safety is strong across boundaries, risks are surfaced early and addressed collaboratively. When it is thin, people calibrate their words, wait for more certainty, or hope the issue will resolve itself.

Even within a single company or project, psychological safety might fluctuate as it lives in the spaces between people. In one project review session, after seeing their team dynamics assessment results, a superintendent paused and reflected:

> "I try to keep communication open, but I'm realizing now that maybe I just assume people will speak up if there is an issue. This makes me wonder who I'm not hearing from."

His comment surfaced a critical blind spot: invitation does not automatically equal safety. In another assessment debrief, a field engineer offered a complementary perspective:

> "The office staff thinks everything's running smoothly. But being out here [in the field], I can tell there is a lot not being said. People just deal with things [e.g., quality issues] quietly."

The field engineer's comment shows how easily silence can give the impression that everything is under control. When people quietly work around problems instead of raising them, leaders may not see the concerns, risks, or frustrations accumulating beneath the surface. Together, these perspectives reveal a gap between a leader's intention to keep communication open and people's actual experience of speaking up.

Figures 15 and 16 illustrate how these internal variations appeared[13] within one project team when analyzed across specific trades and roles. Figure 15 shows that psychological safety ratings varied across trades. Some trades had ratings clustered near the high end, while others had wider spreads extending to lower scores. These differences suggest that people within the same project did not all experience psychological safety in the same way. Notably, trades like electrical and carpenters show broader distributions and lower-end responses compared with several smaller

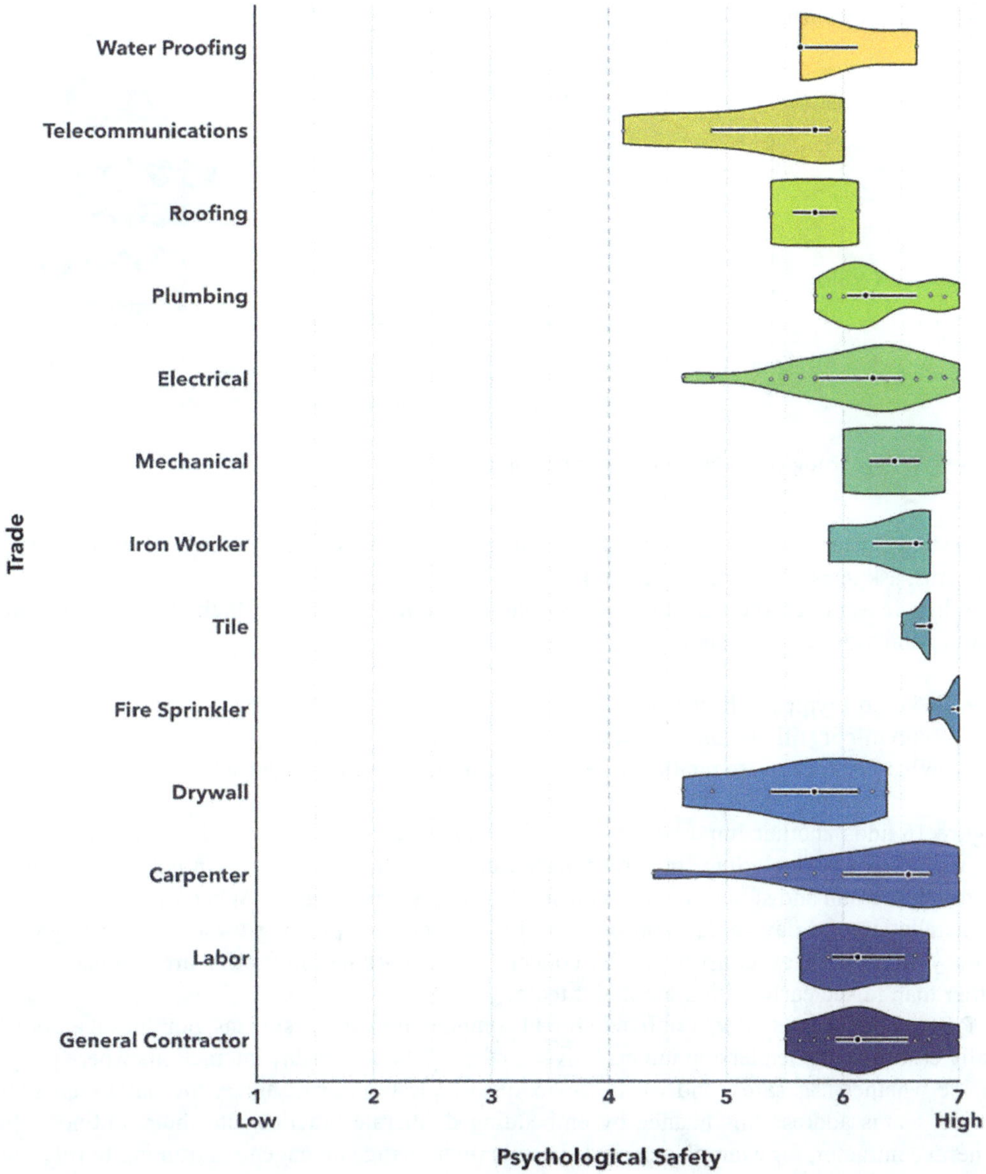

Figure 15 Psychological Safety by Trade at Project A.

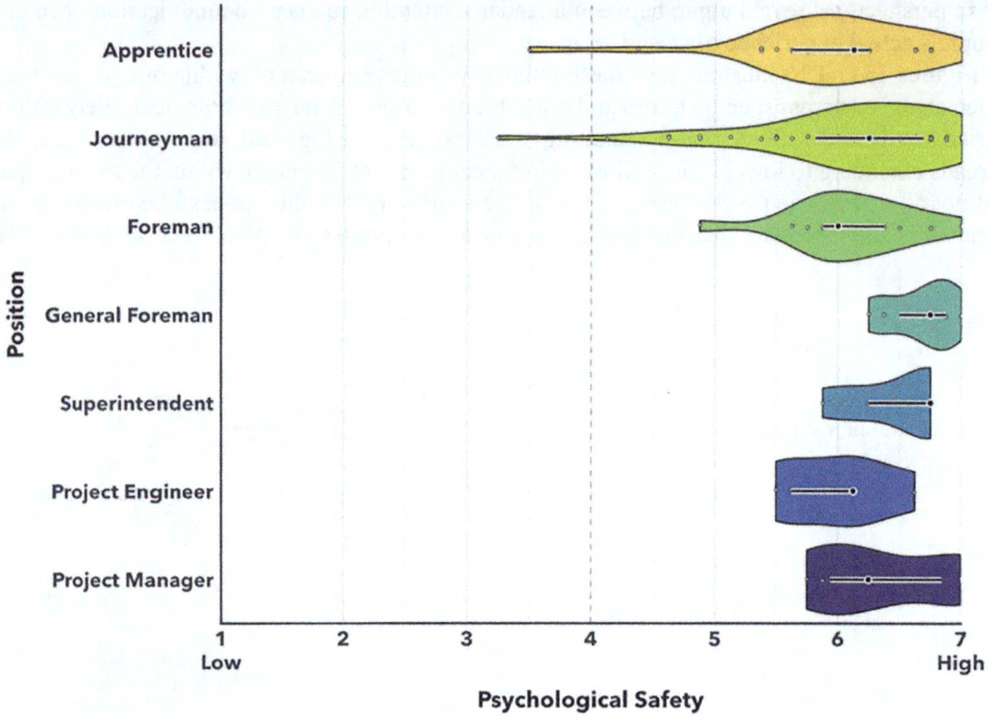

Figure 16 Psychological Safety by Role at Project A.

trades that cluster near the top of the scale—suggesting pockets where it may feel riskier to raise concerns, ask questions, or disagree early.

When leaders see the variation rather than assuming uniformity, their questions become sharper and more consequential:

- Who do I typically hear from?
- Who might still be holding back?
- What is the cost—to quality, schedule, and morale—of that silence?

Figure 16 adds another important nuance: frontline roles (apprentice and journeyman) show the widest range—including some responses well below the midpoint—while leadership roles (general foreman and superintendent) cluster higher and more tightly. When the people closest to installation and day-to-day coordination hesitate before speaking up, the result is greater latency: quality issues, constructability concerns, and coordination friction are handled locally rather than raised early with the broader team.

Psychological safety does not live in broad company policies or slogans, nor does it automatically cascade from leadership intent. It lives in the small, day-to-day interactions where people decide whether it is safe—and worth it—to speak, question, or disagree. We have seen some project teams address this nuance by embedding deliberate practice into their routines. One general contractor, for example, created space in their change management training to role-play high-stakes conversations. They practiced telling a client about a budget overrun. The focus was not only on the technical content but also on the relational execution—the tone, sequencing, transparency, acknowledgment of impact, and shared framing of trade-offs.

Most importantly, they normalized the discomfort of interpersonal risk-taking. They did not pretend it was easy; they treated discomfort as expected in responsible leadership. The initiative reinforced the role of psychological safety in collaboration, risk management, and resilience. Participants in the training were encouraged to wrap up the session by naming one behavior to carry into the next real client meeting—shortening the gap between practice and field application. Teams can build on this kind of practice through small, deliberate actions that help them invite voices that may otherwise go unheard, raise risks earlier, and prepare for difficult conversations across roles and organizational boundaries.

Boundary Conversation Opener

"I want to surface a risk early so we can protect both schedule and quality. We have seen Y condition in Area Z. Here is what we know, here is what we are still validating, and here are two options with trade-offs. What constraints or impacts should we consider together?"

Practice a Boundary Conversation

- Role-play one crucial conversation (e.g., with a client or someone from a different role or function).
- Debrief: What helped? What hurt? What will you do next time?
- Identify one phrase or approach you will use in the next real conversation.

As you think about your team, consider:

- Who may feel safe to speak, and who does not?
- Are there specific patterns among team members?
- Where do the most difficult conversations happen, and how can the people involved be better supported?

Building One Team means paying attention to where safety thins and deliberately lowering the cost of honesty in those spaces. The question shifts from "Do we value speaking up?" to "What are we intentionally doing to make speaking up normal—especially where it matters most?"

1.8 From Awareness to Action

Noticing the patterns is only half the work. The other half is intentionally designing conditions in which speaking up is expected, supported, and acted on. Awareness changes what teams see. Design changes what teams do.

Why Does This Matter Now?

Silence is expensive. It delays responses to problems, hides lessons, and fractures the sense of "we" in a team. Psychological safety is how teams reclaim performance and humanity—together as One Team. Teams that shorten the time between noticing a risk and speaking up make better decisions sooner and avoid rework later. Healthy teams do not eliminate all problems; they reduce the time between noticing a problem and working through it together.

How Do We Co-create It?

Through intentional actions repeated consistently over time. Psychological safety does not scale by accident; it is shaped through signals and systems.

- Signals are the small daily moments that show people what is safe and valued: who gets invited to contribute, how questions are handled, and what happens after someone flags a risk.
- Systems are the routines and structures that reinforce those signals over time: how people are onboarded, how teams plan and review their work, the norms they establish, and whether leaders follow through on what they hear.

People experience psychological safety through daily interactions, but teams and organizations sustain it by consistently reinforcing the behaviors they want to see. What gets reinforced gets repeated.

What Does It Look Like at the Organizational Level?

We have started seeing more companies weave psychological safety into how they operate. Some embed it into onboarding so that, from day one, people learn that asking questions, flagging concerns, and offering feedback are part of the job—not risks to avoid. Others make psychological safety an explicit company objective as part of how they pursue their organizational goals.

When leaders name it publicly and model it consistently, they send a clear message: psychological safety matters, it is not a given, and it should not be treated as such. This is how One Team spreads across an enterprise—when learning and candor are not side initiatives but part of how the organization chooses to work. When goals are visible and behaviors are modeled, people learn that candor is a contribution, not a career risk. Over time, culture shifts not because people are told to speak but because it becomes normal to do so.

Start Small and Start Now

You do not need a full program to begin. You need to start creating spaces where voice feels safer and more useful this week than it was last week. Take a moment to reflect:

- Where does your team stand today?
- Who might not feel heard or safe to speak?
- What is one moment this week when you will lower the cost of speaking and raise the payoff for doing it?

- Which recurring meeting will you modify first (agenda, norms, or follow-through) to promote speaking up?

The road to becoming One Team starts here, with awareness, reflection, and your next step forward.

Psychological Safety in Practice: A Team Checklist

Invite voice.

- Invite people to speak early, especially those who are quieter or newer to the team.
- Create opportunities for everyone to contribute without allowing hierarchy to steer the conversation.
- Ask for concerns before confidence: "What could go wrong?" before "Are we good?"

Make it safe to ask and disagree.

- Welcome questions at every stage, from planning through installation.
- Make space for disagreement before deciding. Ask: "What concerns or alternative perspectives have we not yet considered?"
- Disagree with ideas, not people; use "I see it differently because . . ."

Respond in ways that increase safety.

- Thank the person who surfaced a risk.
- Replace blame with curiosity: "What made this hard?" "What did we miss?"
- Correct privately; learn publicly; address behaviors and systems, not identities.

Close the loop.

- End meetings with: We heard / We will / By when.
- Track input visibly (team board/channel) so voice does not disappear.
- Verify completion—do not just assign; confirm that it is done.

Learn fast.

- Keep a visible learning log: What happened/What we learned/What will change.
- Celebrate "early flags" and "good catches" (the prevention wins).
- Celebrate incremental improvements over perfect scores.

Protect the conditions for voice.

- Design a fast, blame-free response path.
- If someone raises a concern, pause work long enough to address it.
- If you cannot act, explain why and what you can do instead (transparency builds trust).

If your team is wondering where to begin, Table 1 offers a simple seven-day starter plan to help move this work from concept to practice. The sequence is intentionally cumulative: first make the current reality visible, then name what you notice, protect the conditions for voice, practice new behaviors, reinforce them, track what happens, and close the loop. The goal is not to fix everything in a week but to create momentum through small, visible actions that show people speaking up is both safer and more worthwhile.

Table 1 Sample 7-Day Starter Plan

Day	*Purpose*	*Action*
See it	Get a quick read on how psychological safety is currently experienced across the team	Invite team members to reflect on how safe it feels to speak up today using one of the tools described earlier. Pay attention to differences in people's experiences and whose voices may be heard less often.
Name it	Make what you noticed visible and discussable	Share back patterns from the pulse check without identifying individuals. Ask what resonates or surprises the team, and keep the tone curious, not judgmental.
Protect it	Lower the cost of speaking up	Introduce one norm that supports voice, such as "Questions are expected" or "Clarifying before acting is a sign of care." Post it somewhere visible and reinforce it during daily work.
Practice it	Rehearse the behavior you want to see more often	Role-play one real scenario or replay a recent moment where someone hesitated. Practice language people can use to ask a question, disagree, request help, or raise a concern.
Reinforce it	Reinforce the behavior	In a team huddle or recap, recognize one person who raised a question, surfaced a risk, or spoke up early. Explain how it helped the team prevent a problem, learn, or respond sooner.
Track it	Show that voice leads to action	Start a simple "Voice → Action" log. Capture one thing the team raised, what the team will do in response, who owns it, and by when.
Close the loop	Turn the week into a repeatable practice	Report back on one thing you heard, what you did about it, and what will happen next. End by asking "What is one small change we can make next week to help questions, concerns, and ideas surface earlier?"

What about metrics? Look for observable changes in how people speak up and how the team responds. Are concerns surfacing earlier? Are more voices being heard? Does input lead to visible follow-through? Choose two or three signals to watch over the next few weeks:

- Speed of surfacing: Are risks, questions, and concerns showing up earlier—before they become rework, conflict, or late surprises?
- Range of voices: Are you hearing from the quieter, newer, or more junior people—not just the usual confident contributors?
- Response quality: When someone speaks up, do they receive curiosity, appreciation, and follow-through—or defensiveness, dismissal, or silence?
- Learning visibility: Are mistakes and near misses turning into shared lessons and small changes, or turning into silence and workarounds?

Make progress visible:

- Create a simple "Voice → Action" log (spreadsheet, whiteboard, notebook, or pinned message). Each entry is one line: What we heard/What we will do/Owner/By when

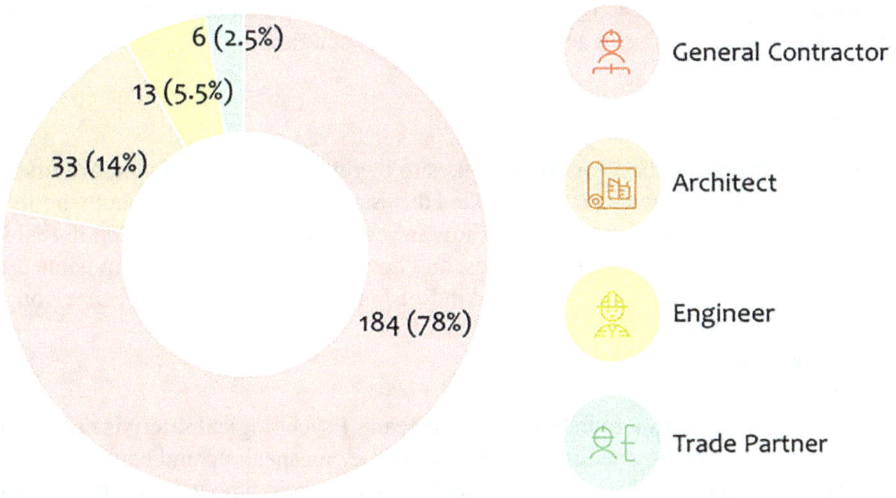

Figure 17 Quality Issues Reported by Company Type.

- Review it weekly and answer: What moved? What got stuck?
- Close the loop publicly when something changes—even something small. Closing the loop is what makes speaking up feel worth it.

The goal is not getting high scores—it is shorter silence, earlier truth, and clearer follow-through. For instance, Figure 17 shows the number of quality issue entries submitted by company type at Project C. In this snapshot, the general contractor authored 184 entries, the architects authored 33, the engineers 13, and trade partners only 6. This distribution is a signal—not about who cares but about who feels safe (and motivated) to report. In construction, trade partners are the ones that spend the most time in the field. They are the ones installing the work, noticing defects as they emerge, and seeing quality drift before anyone else. When trade partners scarcely show up in the reporting stream, it rarely means "they are not seeing issues." More often, it means that the system is making reporting feel costly, confusing, or futile.

Use this figure as a practical voice check. Instead of asking, "Why are trade partners not reporting?" ask questions that reveal the work conditions:

- Is the reporting channel easy to access in the field (phone, language, time, steps)?
- Does raising an issue create social risk (blame, pushback, reputation) or production risk (work interruption, delay, or rework)?
- Do trade partners see visible follow-through—or do reports disappear into a black hole?
- Are we rewarding speed and silence more than early problem detection?

When teams use what they observe to invite more voices, respond constructively, and follow through consistently, the conditions that support psychological safety become part of the team's everyday way of working. The shift from "we should" to "we do" becomes visible in meetings, in how quickly risks surface, in whose voices are heard, and in the trust that builds when the loop is closed. Keep the approach simple and visible, and focus on steady progress: one small improvement and one meaningful act of follow-through at a time.

1.9 Highlights

This chapter laid the foundation for what it takes to begin building One Team. We first looked beneath the surface—at silence, fear, futility, and the assumptions we carry about who feels safe and who does not. From there, we explored how psychological safety shows up in real behaviors, how it varies across roles and boundaries, and how teams can make this invisible dynamic visible. Building One Team starts with this kind of honest examination—because you cannot strengthen what you have not first learned to see.

Key ideas explored:

1. Psychological safety as a foundation of One Team: Psychological safety is not about comfort; it is about creating conditions in which people can speak up and contribute. It shapes whether truth travels early or late—whether risks surface in time to solve them or accumulate quietly into rework and strain. Psychological safety helps people move from guarding themselves to engaging honestly with the work and with one another. Without it, collaboration becomes compliance. With it, teams can coordinate, learn, and improve together.
2. Silence is often a signal: Fear asks, "What will this cost me?" Futility asks, "Will anything change?" Both shape behavior long before a word is spoken. When teams learn to look into silence—not just at what is said—they uncover the hidden barriers that stall performance and erode trust.
3. Exploring safety as a team: Psychological safety becomes clearer when teams pause to examine it together. Simple assessments and conversations help surface hidden variation—who feels safe, where it drops, and why. These tools make the invisible visible so dialogue can deepen and improvement can be shared. A shared snapshot helps teams move from assumptions ("we are fine") to reality ("here is where we are now") to improvement ("here is what we will work on").
4. Safety can be uneven: Psychological safety shifts across roles, relationships, and boundaries. Someone may feel safe with peers but hesitate with a supervisor. A team may feel aligned internally but guarded with external stakeholders. Examining these differences helps teams identify the relationships and situations where people are more likely to hesitate—and where greater intention is needed to make speaking up safe and worthwhile.
5. Behaviors can build or break safety: Psychological safety lives in micro-interactions—how questions are received, how mistakes are handled, and whether feedback leads to visible change. Environments teach people what is safe—and what is worth it. *In healthy teams, the response after someone speaks matters as much as the speaking.*
6. Awareness must become design: Insight alone does not shift culture. Teams move from "we should" to "we do" when they build routines that invite voice, protect candor, and close the loop. Psychological safety grows through intentional signals and reinforcing systems—through practice, not intention alone.

Healthy teams are not teams without friction. They are teams with enough safety and follow-through to turn friction into learning instead of letting it become fear, silence, or blame. That begins when people are willing to bring the friction into the conversation—naming the concern, the mistake, the question, or the disagreement while there is still time to learn from it together.

Psychological safety creates permission to do so. It gives people the social clearance to ask, admit, question, and challenge. But permission alone is not enough. Permission must be met with action: with respectful response, shared problem-solving, and visible follow-through.

In the next chapters, we move from creating permission to building habits—from the conditions that allow voice to the behaviors that sustain connection.

Notes

1 For context, construction teams are often made up of two broad groups: the administrative side (commonly referred to as staff or admin) and the field side (commonly referred to as craft). Within the field, common roles include apprentices, journeymen, and foremen.

2 In construction, a "macho culture" usually refers to an informal set of norms that equate competence and leadership with toughness, emotional restraint, and self-reliance—often expressed as "handle it," "do not complain," "do not look weak," and "just get it done." Hanna et al. (2020) describe construction as a context where dominant masculine norms—such as stoicism, emotional restraint, toughness, competitiveness, and risk-taking—can become informal expectations for what "competent" work looks like.

3 Researchers whose work has strongly influenced how psychological safety, voice, and silence are understood—and has informed this book—include:

- Amy Edmondson, Novartis Professor of Leadership and Management at the Harvard Business School.
- Jim Detert, Professor of Business Administration and Public Policy at the University of Virginia.
- Ethan Burris, Professor of Management at the University of Texas at Austin.

4 Edmondson (1999) defined team psychological safety as a shared belief that the team is safe for interpersonal risk-taking—a condition that supports speaking up, asking for help, admitting mistakes, and learning.

5 "Quitting before leaving" captures the psychology behind learned futility: as people detach, they conserve effort and stop voicing improvement ideas—not because they do not care but because they have concluded it will not matter; it is a crisp mechanism for how futility chokes learning long before anyone actually exits (Burris et al. 2008).

6 Detert and Edmondson (2011) describe how teams often operate with unspoken "rules" about when it is acceptable to speak up. These taken-for-granted beliefs include ideas like "do not embarrass your boss," "do not bypass hierarchy," or "loyalty means not making waves." These implicit "voice theories" can make silence feel sensible—even responsible—because speaking up is framed as disrespectful, risky, or disruptive. When those beliefs go unnamed, they quietly reinforce both fear and futility. Naming them is often the first step to loosening their grip and creating new norms for candor.

7 For ease of visualization, the sticky notes containing a checkmark were highlighted with circles. Each sticky note with a circle represents one participant who indicated that they had remained silent even though they had something to contribute.

8 Schein and Bennis (1965) introduced psychological safety in the context of organizational change, describing it as the feeling that someone can face change without losing their identity, integrity, or membership in groups they care about. Kahn (1990) broadened the concept and defined psychological safety as "feeling able to show and employ one's self without fear of negative consequences to self-image, status, or career." Edmondson (1999) brought the concept into the team setting as the belief that one can take interpersonal risks—like speaking up, admitting mistakes, or offering ideas—without fear of punishment or humiliation. In Gomez et al. (2019), we further described psychological safety as being shaped by real-time assessments people make about what is likely to happen if they speak up. Before someone raises a concern, asks for help, admits a mistake, or offers an idea, they quickly scan the room—often unconsciously—and estimate the relational, reputational, or practical impact of doing so. These split-second social calculations influence behavior in powerful ways.

9 Lean (and Lean Construction) is often grounded in two foundational principles: respect for people and continuous improvement. Psychological safety is one of the conditions that allows these principles to move from aspiration to practice. Teams cannot continuously improve if people do not feel safe to surface problems, question decisions, or admit mistakes. For readers interested in the relationship

between psychological safety and lean, our research further explores this connection and can be found in publications available through the International Group for Lean Construction (IGLC) library.

10 Assessment developed as part of Gomez's (2023) dissertation and available at www.sulyngomez.com

11 Amy's book, *The Fearless Organization* (2018), explains what psychological safety is, why it matters for learning and performance, and how leaders shape it through everyday signals.

12 We often use digital polling tools such as Mentimeter or Slido, which allow anonymous responses and real-time visualization of group patterns.

13 In both figures, each "violin" shows the spread of responses (wider = more people clustered there), with the marker highlighting the center of the distribution—so you can see not only the average level of safety but also how consistent (or uneven) the experience is across the group.

Chapter 2

Go Back to Basics

Respect for People

Psychological safety answers, "Can I say it?" Respect is revealed in what happens after I do. It is shown in how we treat one another: how we invite input, how we listen, how we disagree, how we give feedback, and how we follow through. It is that steady response—repeated over time—that turns "me" into "we" and helps a team begin to operate as One.

Respect Felt, Not Assumed: A Journey of Growth

Before writing it here, I had shared this story only once in my life. Even now, writing this brings a lump to my throat. Growing up, I took my role as the "responsible one" very seriously. As the eldest, I saw myself as the protector—the one who "knew best." I believed, deeply, that respect had to be earned. To me, it was conditional, something granted only to those who met a certain standard.

That belief shaped how I approached much of life, including my relationships with my siblings. With a mistaken understanding of what it meant to care for them, I tried to "protect" them, steer them away from mistakes, and make sure they stayed on the "right" path. I wanted them to be safe, to succeed, and to avoid the painful experiences I had faced. But in trying so hard to show them my way, I created a rigid environment in which my approval seemed necessary for their choices to feel valid. Unintentionally, I disrespected their autonomy, their need to make their own choices, and their right to learn in their own way. Instead of giving them space to grow, I was holding them to a standard that left no room for their own experiences or perspectives.

When they came to me with ideas or fears, I often jumped straight into a fixing mode. I rarely paused to ask what they wanted or needed. I wanted the best for them, but I was creating an unhealthy environment—one with pressure to agree with me, to perform for me, and to avoid disappointing me.

Eventually, I began to notice the limits of my approach. I was so focused on being right that I dismissed what they were telling me. And I deeply regret it. Looking back, I can see how lonely that must have felt—coming to me for connection and getting lectured instead. My way

DOI: 10.1201/9781003734864-2

of seeing things back then was not helping them grow, and it certainly was not showing respect. The result? Silence and distance—both of which I'm still working to heal.

My *aha moment* did not come all at once. It was the culmination of a much longer journey of noticing, reflecting, (un)learning, and gradually coming to see respect differently: Respect is not something we offer only after someone proves they deserve it; it is something we extend from the beginning, giving people room to become who they are capable of being.

Over the years, I have met wonderful people—teachers, mentors, colleagues—who showed me by example that respect was the starting point, not a prize. They did not wait for me to "earn" their respect. They started from the assumption that I belonged in the room, that my questions mattered, and that I was capable of learning and contributing to the team. Their respect showed up in concrete ways: they made time for me despite their busy schedules, showed me patience when I was still figuring things out, and gave me opportunities I had not yet learned how to ask for. They listened without rushing to correct me. They opened doors—introductions, invitations, projects, feedback—and then stayed close enough to help me walk through them. And they never made me feel like I had to pass a test to deserve basic human dignity.

This personal shift—from "people must earn my respect" to "I will begin with respect and build from there"—has reshaped how I show up as a leader, teammate, and family member. I still care about performance. But I no longer mistake rigid expectations for respect. Now, I see respect as creating conditions where others can develop their own voice, capabilities, and judgment, rather than conforming to mine.

As I learned more about psychological safety, I started paying attention to who spoke first, who stayed silent, and what happened after someone raised a concern. I noticed how quickly a team can interpret politeness as respect or assume "no complaints" means "people feel safe." Respect, however, lives in what we say and what we do—especially when someone is still learning, when they are struggling, or when they see the world differently than we do.

As part of a broader research initiative on psychological safety in construction, I had the opportunity to work closely with teams to understand how they were functioning. The leadership of one of these teams believed that everyone on the team, both staff and craftworkers, felt respected and valued. When we looked at the data, a more nuanced picture emerged. Staff members generally reported feeling high levels of respect and psychological safety. Field crews, particularly craftworkers, described a different experience. Their responses were more cautious and guarded. They felt pressure to deliver, but not always permission to question, slow down, or suggest a better way. Speaking up often felt risky.

In follow-up interviews, craftworkers described everyday interactions that made the environment feel less respectful and less safe. These included being called by unwanted nicknames or labels—such as "the slow one" or "the newbie"—instead of by their names, and being met with mocking or dismissive responses when they asked for help or made a request. What some may intend as harmless joking can signal that asking questions or seeking help carries social risk, especially across differences in language, culture, or power.

Respect began with listening—and acting.

Knowing this, the project team and I translated those insights into simple shifts: use names, not labels; check your tone when you are tired or under pressure; and if a joke lands wrong, name it and repair it ("That did not come out right—sorry, Juan. Thanks for raising the issue."). Leaders modeled this and added brief reminders to huddles: respect in tone and words.

Then we asked a bigger question: how do we make these changes stick? That question led directly to the development of a craft recognition program to foster connection and reinforce the very behaviors craftworkers told us mattered most.

This program began by creating more intentional opportunities for people to connect across roles, companies, and languages. One of its first components was a series of bilingual sessions that brought people together to learn and share a meal. Craftworkers helped choose the food and, at times, prepared dishes on the jobsite that reflected their cultures and traditions. These gatherings created space to learn and correctly pronounce one another's names, build relationships across roles and companies, and recognize the people behind the work.

Another powerful piece of the program was the Golden Ticket. Anyone on the project, regardless of their company or role, could give or receive a Golden Ticket to recognize someone for kindness, helpfulness, or support. Respect was shown through the appreciation of each person's contributions to the team. The team celebrated contributions publicly and turned "be respectful" into behaviors that anyone could spot and repeat.

All the activities in the program were thoughtful signals: "We see you. You matter. Your voice and your work matter." Respect became visible, tangible, and shared. One of the superintendents captured the shift: "We realized we were not being disrespectful—but we were not being intentional about it either. And that is what changed. We started showing respect on purpose."

As these efforts unfolded, something began to shift. The craftworkers began to participate more. The interactions between teams grew warmer. You could feel the difference. People described feeling proud when their ideas were implemented and, just as importantly, they began to expect backup—not blowback—when they spoke up. Respect created a reliable social contract: if you surface a risk, we respond with dignity and follow-through.

Respect was not assumed. It was shown. It was felt. And it became the foundation for something greater, the possibility of becoming One Team.

In the sections that follow, we move from respect as a value to respect as a set of visible, repeatable behaviors. We clear up common myths that dilute respect into politeness or silence and walk through real scenarios that show what respect looks like in the flow of work—especially under pressure. By the end of this chapter, you will be able to:

1. Explain why respect is psychological safety's daily language—and how it shapes whether speaking up feels worth it in real time.
2. Recognize what respect is not (e.g., not "be nice," not avoidance, not lowering standards) so teams do not confuse respect with comfort or compliance.
3. Spot the small signals that erode respect and name how those signals teach people what is safe to say and what is smart to hide.
4. Facilitate conversations to surface patterns of respect and disrespect—then translate insights into specific behavior shifts.
5. Apply practical respect-in-action moves so respect becomes consistent in the daily rhythm of work.

2.1 Starting With a Basic Exploration Through Reflection

A parable allows people to talk about behaviors with some distance before bringing the conversation closer to home. In our work with construction teams, we often use an adapted version of the well-known story "El hipopótamo sin respeto (Hugo the Hippopotamus)." The goal of the original tale helps children recognize how their behavior affects others and develop empathy. Our version draws on feedback from staff and craftworkers on construction projects to illustrate behaviors they experienced as disrespectful:

> Hugo was known for getting things done. He moved fast, talked fast, and expected everyone else to keep up.
>
> Every morning, Hugo arrived in a rush. He parked wherever was most convenient, even when the spot was meant for deliveries or someone with a designated pass. He walked into the trailer, grabbed coffee, left a mess on the counter, and headed out without a second thought. On the surface, none of it seemed like a big deal. But the message was clear: my time matters more than yours, and someone else will deal with the rest.
>
> The same pattern showed up in how he worked with others.
>
> If Hugo needed a charger, a tablet, a drill, or a chair, he used whatever was closest—even if it belonged to someone else. He rarely returned things where he found them. People spent extra time looking for tools and asking around. No one confronted him directly. They just started hiding what they needed, labeling everything more aggressively, or working around him when they could.
>
> In meetings, Hugo had a way of making people feel small without ever raising his voice much. If someone asked a clarifying question during a huddle, he would sigh and say, "We have already gone over this." If a newer team member offered an idea, he might laugh and reply, "Let's leave that to the people who have been doing this for a while."
>
> Sometimes he used nicknames instead of names. "The new guy." "Princess." "Bossy." A few people laughed along. Most stayed quiet.
>
> One afternoon, during a coordination meeting, a project engineer pointed out that a layout issue might create a conflict in the field. She had taken the time to compare drawings, check dimensions, and flag the concern early. Hugo barely looked up. He rolled his eyes, said, "We don't have time to chase every little possibility," and moved on. Nobody pushed back. A few days later, the issue showed up exactly where she had predicted. Work stopped. People scrambled. Time was lost. Frustration spread.
>
> No one said, "This could have been prevented if we had listened."
>
> But several people were thinking about it.
>
> That was the pattern with Hugo. Concerns were raised, then minimized. Questions were asked, then shut down. Small signals accumulated. People began to calculate: Is it worth saying this out loud? Will I get help, or will I get embarrassed? More and more often, silence felt safer.
>
> Even safety conversations changed. When someone mentioned a near miss, Hugo brushed it off as "part of the job." When a foreman tried to explain that the crew needed a little more time to do it right, Hugo heard it as resistance instead of care.
>
> None of this looked dramatic from the outside. No screaming meltdowns. No one stormed off the site. But you could see it: People shared less. They asked fewer questions. The job kept moving forward. But the team paid the price.

On most teams, lack of respect rarely arrives as shouting but rather leaks in through small signals that teach people what is safe to say and what is smart to hide, for example:

- Talking over someone or interrupting mid-sentence.
- Eye rolls, sighs, or smirks when a question is asked.

- Using labels instead of names.
- Sarcasm or a mocking tone.
- Taking shared tools and not returning them.
- Leaving shared spaces messy.
- Not crediting ideas or explaining someone's idea as if it were your own.
- Excluding people from plans that affect their work.
- Failing to close the loop after someone raises a risk ("Thanks—we will update you") and never doing it.

Facilitation Prompt

When introducing this story to your team, read it out loud and ask participants to write down the behaviors they experience as disrespectful. When helpful, adapt a few details to reflect your team's context (tools, huddles, trailers, emails) so the story resonates with your team.

Why this story? Hugo brings together familiar behaviors that may seem small but can gradually erode respect and psychological safety: ignoring shared norms, creating messes others have to clean, using tone to shut people down. The story helps teams recognize these patterns without singling anyone out.

Disrespect rarely explodes into the room—it accumulates quietly. Small signals teach people what is safe to say and what is better left unsaid. Use the story as a starting point to discuss what feels familiar, what may be showing up in the team's own interactions, and how it affects others. Then agree on one habit to start and one habit to stop during the coming weeks, and decide how the team will keep those commitments visible. This is one way healthy teams shorten the distance between noticing disrespect and redesigning the behavior.

Debrief

What feels familiar in your team? What would one step toward greater respect look like next week?

Team Commitments (Choose or Adapt for Your Team)

- When someone raises a question or concern, pause before responding. Ask one genuine follow-up question to understand what they are seeing.
- Before giving direction or making a decision that affects others' work, invite their perspective and consider what they know that you may not.
- If your words, tone, or actions cause someone to feel dismissed or disrespected, acknowledge it, apologize, and clarify what you will do differently.
- When someone speaks up, close the loop by explaining what will happen next—even when the answer is that no action will be taken.

Make It Stick

At the end of the week, hold a brief check-in: Did we follow through on our commitment? What difference did it make? What should we start, stop, or continue doing? Name what worked and reinforce it. If the commitment did not hold, discuss what got in the way, adjust it, and try again.

What to watch for as evidence: earlier questions in huddles, fewer dismissive side comments or eye rolls, faster resolution of issues, greater transparency, and visible close-the-loop updates.

The team introduced earlier in this chapter also went through this exercise. Figure 18 grew out of what we learned from their experience and captures their journey—from assuming respect was present to intentionally designing it. It shows how teams move from unintentional blind spots to deliberate, lived respect.

In this team's journey, people initially felt unseen. This often looks like silence in meetings, guarded feedback, or "just get it done" compliance.

The first shift is Awareness—acknowledging reality and naming the gap with integrity and candor. This is where teams say, "We thought we were being respectful, but we were not being intentional." Without this step, improvement remains superficial.

As awareness grew, the team developed readiness—the decision to create conditions for meaningful action. This is where the team moves beyond good intentions and designs routines that invite voice, support participation, and translate feedback into visible change. Empowerment is not declared; it is structured. Huddles, recognition programs, loop-closing practices, and tone resets become intentional.

As those conditions strengthened, a greater sense of belonging emerged—teams actively embrace differences and build connection through presence and empathy. People feel seen not just as workers but as individuals with identities, backgrounds, and insights that matter. At this stage, respect is no longer assumed. It is felt consistently in how work is planned, how feedback

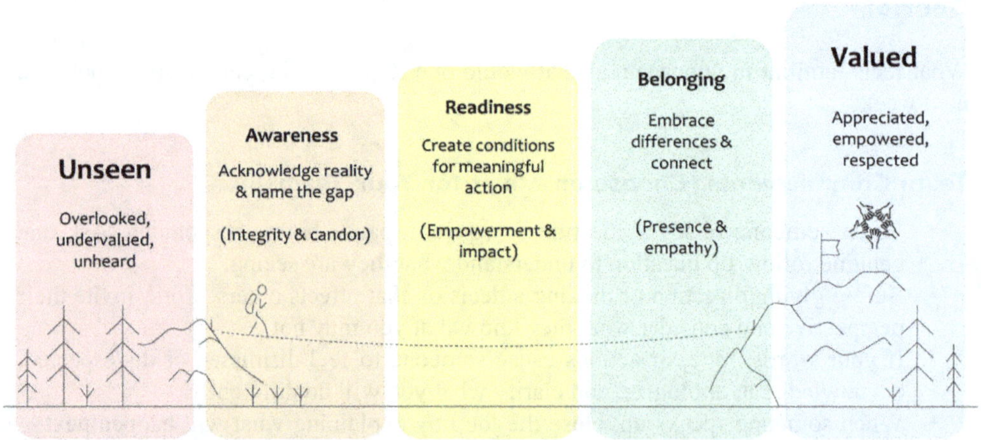

Figure 18 From Unseen to Valued—A Developmental Path Toward One Team.

is handled, and how recognition is shared. Connection becomes part of how the team operates, not a side initiative.

The final state—Valued—captures what changes over time: feedback loops close, recognition becomes visible, and respect is shown consistently in daily routines. At this point, respect is no longer something the team talks about as an abstract concept; it is something people can reliably feel in the way they are treated, heard, and supported.

Respect becomes practical once a team can see it in everyday moments. But there is a common pitfall: as soon as you name "respect," people often translate it into comfort or avoiding conflict. Before we go further, we need to draw clear boundaries—so respect does not get diluted into politeness or misused to lower standards and dodge accountability.

2.2 Understanding What Respect Is Not About

Respect is not code for "be nice," "agree with everything," or "lower the bar." It is not avoiding hard conversations, tiptoeing around problems, or handing out perks to keep people quiet. Respect is not deference to title or seniority, and it is definitely not silence when something is unsafe or unclear. Healthy teams do not trade respect for speed; they use respect to move faster with fewer surprises and less rework.

Figure 19 illustrates common misconceptions about respect and how we can start reframing them.

Respect is not a vibe; it is a set of repeatable moves. Practice the moves, and psychological safety gets stronger—because people learn, through experience, that honesty will be met with dignity and follow-through. And when those moves are consistent, teams do not just "get along"—they stay healthy even under pressure, because people can disagree, learn, and repair without fear. Once you clear up what respect is not, the question becomes: what does it look like when respect is embedded in a team's way of working together?

2.3 Lessons in Respect for People

The following scenarios illustrate how respect for people shows up in practice—not just in what leaders say, but in how teams plan, improve, develop, recognize, and care for one another. In each scenario, respect is not "extra." Respect is how the team protects the work and the relationship at the same time. Healthy teams do not treat performance and relationships as competing priorities. Performance improves when the people doing the work are fully engaged and able to contribute their best—asking questions, offering ideas, and helping solve problems—because the team has repeatedly shown that their input is welcomed and acted on.

Scenario 1: Plan With the People Who Do the Work

On a large data center project, the general contractor was preparing for the installation of a key scope of work: the installation of a metallic mesh over metal stud frames (Figure 20). The crew assigned to the work was a drywall team. Although these workers had extensive experience installing metal stud frames on other projects, this type of mesh was new to them.

Before the work began, the project superintendent, Pedro held a planning meeting with the foremen and a group of craftworkers who were assigned to the task. Rather than simply

Respect Myths vs. Reality

	Belief	Impact	Reframe
Respect equals authority	Higher rank deserves more respect	People with less formal power feel less valued	Respect is about humanity
Respect means avoiding disagreement	Avoid disagreement to keep the peace	Teams drift into fake harmony	Respectful dissent is a gift
Respect is (over) protection or control	Steer others so they do not fail	People feel micromanaged, not trusted	Respect supports autonomy without taking over
Respect is being "nice" and quiet	If no one is visibly upset, respect must be present	Harmful behaviors get excused	Genuine respect includes honest feedback and boundary-setting
Respect is performance-based	Respect is conditional (must be earned)	Some people "deserve" respect more	Respect is unconditional
Respect means letting things slide	Being "kind" means going easy	Standards drift and problems repeat	Pair clarity with care
Respect equals sameness	Treat everyone the same way	Different needs and risks get ignored	Treat people fairly
Respect is static	We either have it, or we do not	Complacency and weak maintenance	Respect is shown in practice
Respect is "being yourself" without limits	Being authentic means not having to adjust for others	Boundaries get crossed	Bring your authentic self while being mindful of others' boundaries

Figure 19 Reframing Myths About Respect.

giving them a set of instructions, Pedro invited open discussion by asking, "What safety risks do you see that we should address before we start?" To ground the conversation in the actual work, he had brought in a sample of the metallic mesh, allowing the workers to examine it firsthand.

Figure 20 Metallic Mesh Installed by Drywall Crew.

The workers, who were initially surprised by the opportunity to weigh in, inspected the material closely. One worker, Benjamin, quickly pointed out that each piece of mesh was not only heavy but had sharp edges that could pose serious safety risks during handling and installation. He suggested that, instead of working in pairs as drywall crews usually do, they should work in three-person crews. Two workers would hold the mesh steady and secure it in place, while a third would cut and fasten it to the frames. He believed this setup would be safer and more efficient, reducing the likelihood of injuries and the disruptions they could cause. Benjamin also recommended that the team wear specialized gloves to protect their hands from the sharp edges.

Pedro recognized the value of Benjamin's suggestions. Not only did he accept them on the spot, but he also took it a step further by organizing a dry run where the team could test this approach. During this dry run, workers refined each step, ensuring that the process was both safe and efficient. The dry run went smoothly, and the team confirmed that the process they had helped develop worked well. By involving the workers in planning, they collectively developed a safer, more reliable process. "If we had planned to install the mesh with fewer people," Pedro explained, "we would have risked it becoming unstable. If it suddenly shifted, someone's hand could easily get cut, which would delay the work, increase costs, and create even bigger problems."

The result? Zero safety incidents during this phase of the project and a smoother installation than originally expected. Crew members felt more invested in the work because their insights were implemented, strengthening their commitment to the task. By incorporating the workers' ideas into the plan, Pedro demonstrated respect for their experience and perspectives.

Respect here meant asking the people closest to the work for their input, listening to what they saw, and treating them as partners in planning, not just hands to execute a plan made elsewhere. In One Team, the plan is owned by the people who will make it real.

Make It a Habit

Before any non-routine or higher-risk task, review the work with the people who will perform it. Bring relevant drawings, materials, or mockups into the conversation and ask: "What concerns do you see? What would help us complete this work safely and successfully?" Use their input to adjust or test the plan.

Scenario 2: Empower Everyone to Improve Their Work

At a remote mining project deep in the mountains of Peru, the team was in the middle of a complex phase: installing mechanical, electrical, and plumbing (MEP) systems to transport raw materials from the excavation site to the processing plant. The work had to meet tight deadlines and demanding quality standards. While the project was moving forward as planned, a study of work operations showed some inefficiencies in the workflow. Procurement delays, extended walking distances to retrieve tools, and congestion in the work zones were slowing progress.

Rather than relying solely on project staff to identify and address these inefficiencies, the project manager, Alessandra, turned to the people most familiar with the daily tasks: the workers. She understood that the workers on the front lines often have the best insights into improving workflow. She also knew that creating time for the team to think and reflect on how to improve was critical to the project's success. Alessandra initiated a series of short, weekly "Improvement Huddles." These meetings (Figure 21), held directly on the job site, included not only foremen and supervisors but also the craftworkers responsible for the actual installation of work. During

Figure 21 Project Team Meeting to Discuss Opportunities for Improvement.

the first meeting, she made it clear that everyone's voice was not only welcome but also needed, saying, "You are the experts. We want to hear your ideas for how we can do this better."

Rosa, one of the pipefitters, had noticed that workers were losing valuable time walking long distances to retrieve tools and materials from a storage area far from the work zones. This constant back-and-forth disrupted the flow of work, causing delays. She suggested creating a "mobile tool station." Within days, a cart was modified to serve this purpose. The results were immediate. Workers spent far less time walking back and forth, which led to a smoother workflow. Seeing quick wins, others proposed additional changes. A continuous-improvement habit began to form. Workers felt empowered to share their ideas. This fostered an environment where team members—regardless of their role—felt they had the power to influence how the work was done.

Creating dedicated time for reflection and inviting input from everyone demonstrated respect in practice. Rosa reflected on the experience, saying, "It feels good to have some time to think and when one speaks, our ideas are taken seriously. We are out here every day, and we see things that others might miss. Having a voice means we can make the work better and safer for everyone." By allowing workers to take a step back and think critically about their work, Alessandra signaled that their input was valuable. Acting on their ideas strengthened ownership and showed that participation could lead to meaningful change.

Respect here took the form of giving people time to think, treating frontline insight as a key element in planning the work, and following through on the ideas they raised. One Team grows when improvement is everyone's job.

Make It a Habit

Set aside 15 minutes each week for the people doing the work to reflect on what is helping or hindering progress and suggest improvements. Agree on the actions to take, clarify ownership and timing, and report back at the next huddle on what changed, what was learned, and what still needs attention.

Scenario 3: Developing People's Capabilities

When I started working on my undergraduate thesis, I knew very little about cranes. I had curiosity, a stack of articles, and a rough idea of how to map construction processes—but not the practical experience of planning crane operations on a jobsite. Then I met Rafael—project manager, consultant, and teacher—who had just started facilitating a workshop on crane operations (Figure 22). "Audit my class," he said. "Come to the workshop this weekend. Watch. Ask whatever you need." He did not start by testing me on what I did not know. He started by opening a door.

The following week, Rafael began teaching me how crane operations are planned. Using a marker and a floor plan, he sketched possible crane locations and explained the decisions behind each one: reach, capacity, swing paths, pedestrian flow, wind conditions, and sequencing. He later brought me along on project visits, where he showed me how to interpret crane specifications and account for the unique constraints of each site like having a school adjacent to the site, and how that constrained the reach of the crane.

Months later, that door he opened changed what I thought was possible for me. I finished my thesis, yes—but I also began to see myself differently. The first time a superintendent asked my opinion on a crane phasing question, I had a point of view and the confidence to voice it. That did not happen because someone told me to "be confident." It happened because someone had helped me build that capability—deliberately, repeatedly, and with the assumption that I could learn.

I began to understand that when you respect someone, you help them grow, not just within the boundaries of their current role, but beyond it, encouraging them to expand their horizons. Rafael's mentorship was an act of respect; he recognized my capacity for growth and helped me see that I could contribute to the industry.

What I learned from Rafael and others has influenced the way I now mentor and develop people. Helping others grow is not just a kind gesture; it is a profound demonstration of respect.

Figure 22 Rafael's Crane Workshop.

Respect for someone's capabilities is not just about acknowledging what they can do today; it is about believing in what they could achieve tomorrow and providing the support and opportunities they need to reach their full potential.

Respect here meant believing in people's potential and creating real opportunities to learn. In One Team, capability-building is not a perk—it is part of how a healthy team works: we grow people on purpose, so learning does not depend on luck.

> **Make It a Habit**
>
> Open one door. Invite someone into a learning experience they might not otherwise have access to—such as a site walk, workshop, shadowing opportunity, design review, or visit to another project—and put it on the calendar so it does not get lost in daily demands. Make time afterward to reflect together: "What did you notice? What did you learn? What questions do you still have?"

Scenario 4: Recognize and Celebrate Contributions

On a busy construction site, the general contractor wanted to strengthen safety and build greater ownership across the jobsite. They formed a Safety Committee with a representative from each trade and set a simple cadence: two walks a month, one hour each. The purpose was clear—to walk the site to observe, learn, and identify opportunities together. Each team carried a clipboard with some questions and two boxes at the top: *Wins* and *Opportunities*. The discipline was to fill both.

Each safety walk was followed by a quick debrief in which committee members shared their findings with the entire group. Later, during the weekly project all-hands meetings, the trades that demonstrated strong practices were recognized, and leaders shared what they had done well. In addition, the opportunities for improvement were shared with their leaders during the weekly coordination meetings. Hearing directly from their own workers about what could be improved gave leaders a clearer view of conditions on the project and strengthened accountability and collaboration. Leaders began to see safety not just as a top-down directive but as a shared responsibility, with every worker contributing to how the site was improved. This practice helped shift the perception of safety from being purely regulatory to something owned and practiced by everyone on site.

On the very first walk, the electricians' work area was well organized. Cords hung on hooks. Someone said, "They thought about the next person." The committee wrote it down under *Wins* and snapped a quick photo. At the next all-hands, leaders called the electricians by name and showed the photo on the screen. They said, "This is what good looks like—and here is why it matters: faster starts, fewer near misses, and less hunt-and-seek." The burrito tickets (Figure 23) served as a tangible expression of appreciation for their efforts. These tickets were a way of saying, "We see the extra effort you are putting in, and we value it." And because *Opportunities* were routed to coordination that same week, fixes did not die on paper. Depending on the severity, some suggestions were addressed right away, and others were scheduled as part of a follow-up plan.

The creation of the Safety Committee and the act of recognizing contributions demonstrated that respecting people is also about showing appreciation for their work, reinforcing that every

Figure 23 Small Gestures Matter.

contribution matters. Each burrito ticket handed out during the safety walks served as a reminder that their contributions were seen, valued, and respected.

Over time, this practice of recognizing contributions had a noticeable impact. Workers began to look forward to the safety walks, not just as a way to improve site conditions but because they knew their efforts would be noticed. The feedback from the committee not only improved the physical conditions of the job site but also boosted morale across trades.

Respect here looked like recognition that reinforced shared ownership: naming the specific behavior, explaining why it mattered to the whole site, and then closing the loop on the opportunities so nothing died in silence. That combination builds One Team because it makes the "we" real—wins are shared, problems are shared, and follow-through is shared.

Make It a Habit

Create a consistent routine for recognizing what is working and addressing what needs attention. Include different trades and roles in the review, recognize specific contributions in front of the broader team, and explain why they mattered. Assign ownership and timing for improvement opportunities, track them until they are resolved, and report back so people can see that their observations led to action.

Scenario 5: Prioritize Wellbeing

Construction work is notorious for being physically demanding for craftworkers. By midweek, you could read the job in people's shoulders—rolled forward from overhead work, tight from lifting, or stiff from ladders and crawl spaces. Stretch cards were posted on the jobsite. Toolbox talks were delivered. Still, fatigue crept in, and with it, small mistakes.

The leadership team took one more step to make care visible. They introduced on-site massage sessions (Figure 24) as part of a wellness program to take care of their people—ten-minute

Figure 24 Massage Session for Craftworkers at the Job Site.

slots focused on backs, necks, and shoulders. They wanted to show that they truly valued the wellbeing of every individual on the site.

The massage sessions quickly became popular among the workers. They appreciated not only the physical relief but also the message the program sent. By investing in these sessions, the leadership team showed that they understood the realities of the job and were willing to go beyond standard work practices in the industry. For many of the workers, this gesture was not just an opportunity for relief from physically demanding work—it was a sign of respect, an acknowledgment that their wellbeing mattered just as much as the work they were contributing to the project.

The team made it clear that these sessions were not just a one-time benefit but a regular part of the project's wellness initiative. The project's leadership highlighted that the long-term success of the project depended not just on hitting deadlines but on keeping the workforce healthy and strong. "You are the backbone of what we are doing here, and taking care of you means we are taking care of the future." These words resonated with the workers, many of whom had rarely experienced such direct concern for their physical and mental health on previous projects.

Respect here was shown by acknowledging the heavy load of the work and investing in taking care of people—not just output—and designing systems so people do not have to choose between their health and their livelihood. One Team means we protect people as part of protecting performance—not instead of it.

Make It a Habit

Build wellbeing into the project's regular routines rather than treating it as an occasional benefit. Ask workers what support would be most useful, remove barriers to participation, and put the agreed actions on the calendar. Encourage leaders and supervisors to participate as well, reinforcing that caring for one's wellbeing is part of doing the work responsibly—not a sign of weakness or a distraction from the job.

In every case, respect did more than make people feel appreciated—it changed what the team was able to do together. Risks surfaced earlier. Ideas were shared openly. Ownership grew. Coordination improved. People were more willing to contribute because the environment showed them that their voice, effort, and humanity mattered. Each scenario reinforces the same idea: respect creates the conditions for people to participate fully, develop their capabilities, and contribute to the team's success. The next section turns these examples into practical, repeatable actions that teams can apply consistently.

2.4 Being Respectful in Action

Respect that fosters psychological safety should be practiced every day, in every interaction. It is a commitment to continually listen, learn, and adjust so people feel valued, capable, and included. Respect is not something we declare; it is a practice that others experience.

Why Does This Matter Now?

When respect is present, people speak up sooner, collaborate more openly, and learn faster. When respect is missing—or assumed—teams pay for it in silence, defensiveness, missed risks, and disengagement. Respect is what keeps the "we" intact in One Team.

What Does It Look Like in Daily Team Interactions?

Respect requires consistency. It is built into the flow of work—when you slow down to include others, ask instead of assuming, and respond to questions or mistakes without embarrassment or blame. Respect becomes visible in the "small" moments: who gets interrupted, whose ideas get credited, how tone shifts under pressure, and whether concerns are addressed or quietly dropped. Here are core actions that make respect visible and felt:

Start With Dignity

- Treat respect as the default—not something people must "earn."
- Separate role/rank from worth: hierarchy may guide decisions, not dignity.
- Show consideration in the way you speak and act, especially when someone is still learning or under pressure.

Listen With Empathy and Curiosity

- Listen to understand before responding.
- Ask questions that surface context and perspective: "What are you seeing?" "What do you need?"
- Reflect back what you heard before offering solutions.
- Create space for all team members to participate, especially those whose perspectives are heard less often.

Honor Diversity, Include, and Elevate

- Recognize and value the different experiences, perspectives, and strengths people bring to the team.

- Avoid labels, nicknames, or "jokes" that diminish or exclude based on background, identity, role, beliefs, or appearance.
- Adapt your approach so different people can participate fully, considering factors such as language, context, and timing.

Develop People's Capabilities

- Provide constructive feedback with tact and sensitivity.
- Offer guidance that builds capability, not dependence.
- Set clear guardrails, then give people room to think, try, make mistakes, and learn.
- Share learning opportunities equitably—do not reserve development for a select few.

Give Feedback With Care and Clarity

- Keep feedback specific and behavioral: describe what happened, explain its impact, and clarify the next step.
- Hold people accountable consistently and fairly; candor is part of respect.
- Address recurring issues early; do not let avoidance pass as kindness.
- When you miss the mark, acknowledge it, apologize when appropriate, and make it right.

Recognize Contributions

- Name specific wins (what someone did and why it mattered).
- Celebrate team and individual progress, especially "prevention" work (risks caught early).
- Recognize contributions in ways that fit the person and the moment.
- Make appreciation visible and genuine.

Pay Attention to Wellbeing

- Notice overload and check in, especially during high-pressure periods.
- Respond promptly to psychological and physical safety concerns; do not minimize, mock, or dismiss them.
- Do not treat care and performance as competing priorities; sustainable performance requires both.

Close the Loop

- When someone raises an issue, respond with: We heard / We will / By when.
- Make follow-through visible and confirm that commitments are completed.
- If you cannot act, explain why and what you can do instead.

Remember, respect is a verb, and it shows in our actions.

What Does It Look Like at the Organizational Level?

Respect scales when leaders make it observable and consistent. Teams strengthen respect when they build routines that:

- Invite and encourage voice.
- Support growth through coaching, learning, and opportunities to improve.
- Recognize contributions so people feel seen and valued.
- Close the loop consistently so people learn that speaking up leads somewhere.

Start Small and Start Now

Start by looking at what your environment is teaching people right now. You do not need a major culture initiative to begin. You need a few deliberate moves that make respect more visible this week than it was last week. Take a moment to reflect:

- Where do you see respect being practiced on your team?
- Where might it be missing, assumed, or unintentionally overlooked?
- What is one way you can show respect in action this week?

2.5 Highlights

This chapter deepened the foundation for becoming One Team by grounding our shared way of working in respect for people. Respect lives in the way we plan with—not for—others, the way we notice and appreciate contributions, the way we create space for every voice, and the way we support each person's growth. It is part of how healthy teams function.

Key ideas explored:

1. Respect is not declared; it is experienced: Respect is not demonstrated by what a team says but by how people are treated in everyday interactions. It shows up in tone, attention, follow-through, and the space people are given to think, question, contribute, and grow. When respect is present, people feel they belong. When it is absent, even subtly, people begin to protect themselves.
2. Respect begins with dignity: A central shift in this chapter was moving away from the belief that people must earn respect before they receive it. Healthy teams start from a different premise: dignity comes first. Respect is not a prize for those who perform well, speak confidently, or hold authority. It is the baseline condition that allows people to learn, contribute, and develop their capabilities.
3. Disrespect often enters through small signals: Respect is often eroded not by a single event, but by repeated micro-signals (e.g., labels, interruptions, sarcasm, dismissive tone, lack of credit, careless follow-through, or jokes that land as humiliation).
4. Respect becomes real when it shapes how work is done: Respect is not separate from performance; it strengthens performance. Planning with the people who do the work leads to safer and better processes. Inviting everyone to improve the work builds ownership and momentum. Developing people's capabilities expands what the team can do over time. Recognizing contributions reinforces shared standards. Respect is not extra. It is embedded in the way healthy teams operate.
5. Respect and psychological safety reinforce one another: Respect makes speaking up feel worthwhile. It signals that questions will not be mocked, ideas will not be dismissed, mistakes will not be used to diminish someone's worth, and concerns will be met with dignity.

Healthy teams are not respectful only when things are calm. They are respectful when the pressure is real, the schedule is tight, and the temptation to rush, dismiss, or control is strongest. That is when respect matters most.

Our question to you is not whether respect matters. It is whether people can actually feel it in the way your team works together. Do your words, tone, decisions, and follow-through teach people that they belong here? Do they make contributions easier—or more costly? In One Team, respect is not the soft side of the work. It is part of the work itself.

In the next chapter, we build on this foundation through active learning. If respect helps create the conditions where people feel valued and included, active learning is what teams do with that openness: they test ideas, surface uncertainty early, and improve together. All this requires voice. Someone has to ask, "What are we missing?" "What did we learn?" or "Is there a better way?"

The road to One Team is paved with respect. It is how we begin—and how we keep moving ahead.

Chapter 3

Cultivate the Mindset

Active Learning

Psychological safety makes voice possible. Active learning determines what we do with that voice. Active learning turns questions, mistakes, and experiments into shared insight, better decisions, and more reliable performance. In this chapter, we explore learning as a team discipline—the habit of pausing, asking, adjusting, and improving in real time. One Team is not built by avoiding mistakes; it is built by amplifying what works, surfacing what does not, and learning forward—together.

Learning Is Ever-Present

Stepping into a Town Hall hosted by a large general contractor—where I had been invited to speak about psychological safety—felt like a big moment for me, fresh out of grad school. I was excited but nervous too. The room was filling with people from across the company: business unit leaders, project managers, project engineers, superintendents, foremen, and craftworkers. It was the kind of room where you could feel the weight of experience before anyone even spoke.

Near the entrance sat a small check-in table. Name tags, markers, and a few giveaway items were spread across the top. A banner stood nearby with a QR code to mark attendance. It looked straightforward enough. I wrote my name on a tag, scanned the code, and took a seat.

But as more people arrived, I began to notice something small—small enough that many might have ignored it, but telling once you saw it. People approaching the check-in table hesitated. Some reached for the swag and walked right past the QR code. Others scanned first and skipped the name tags. A few paused, looked at the table, and then looked around as if searching for clues about the "right" check-in sequence. The craftworkers, in particular, seemed to pause the longest. They stood there for a second, reading the setup and trying to decode what was expected.

So instead of sitting and waiting for the session to begin, I turned the check-in table into a welcome station. I handed out markers and swag, pointed people to the name tags, and guided them toward the QR code. That little shift—helping people navigate the check-in process—became an *aha moment* in my journey, one of my clearest lessons about learning.

DOI: 10.1201/9781003734864-3

It started when Juan walked in.

Juan—now a good friend—picked up a marker and a sheet of name tags. He wrote his name down, then stopped. He had written it in a space where the name tag had already been removed. For a split second, he looked confused. Then he laughed, put his hand on his forehead, and shared what had just happened with the people around him so they would not make the same mistake.

There was no defensiveness. No attempt to hide it. Just a quick, human moment: Oops. There it is.

Then, almost immediately, Juan shifted from noticing the mistake to improving the system. He suggested marking the spaces where tags had already been removed with an "X" so the next person would know which spots had already been used (Figure 25). I loved the idea. We started doing it right away. In a matter of seconds, we improved the process. Check-in became clearer, faster, and less awkward for everyone coming in after him.

That is active learning in one of its simplest forms: notice the breakdown, name it, and adjust the system so the next person does not stumble in the same place.

I was still drawing Xs on the remaining sheets when Cesar walked in.

Cesar had been with the company for five years. He picked up one of the sheets I had not gotten to yet and made the same mistake as Juan. But his reaction was completely different.

He froze.

There was no laugh, no joke, no instinct to turn the mistake into a shared lesson. Instead, he lowered his voice and asked if I had scissors so he could cut out the part with his name on it. It

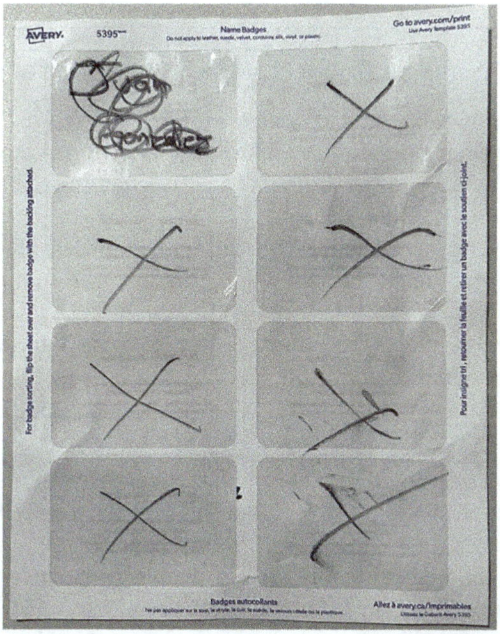

Figure 25 Name Tag Sheet with Juan's Solution for Making Visible the Spaces Where Tags Had Been Removed.

felt like a quick attempt to erase the evidence before anyone noticed. I told him it was okay. He still looked uncomfortable. Only when I offered to throw the whole page away did his shoulders relax. He thanked me, quietly, and walked to his seat.

I never forgot that contrast.

Juan and Cesar made the same low-stakes mistake, just minutes apart, at the same table, in the same room. But they experienced it differently. One made it visible and improved the process. The other tried to hide it and move on as quickly as possible. Watching them side by side, I saw something I had studied for years suddenly playing out in front of me: psychological safety shapes what people do in the moment they feel exposed.

When people believe a mistake will damage how others see them, learning slows down. Not because they stop caring but because they shift their energy toward self-protection. They hide, patch, minimize, or stay quiet. And if that happens around a name tag at a check-in table, imagine what happens when the mistake is tied to budget, schedule, quality, or reputation. People do not suddenly become more open under higher stakes.

Juan's response showed the other path. He made the mistake discussable. He offered an idea. The people around him learned. The system improved. The real win was not simply that he handled the embarrassment well; it was that one person's slip became shared learning for everyone else.

And that is the heart of active learning. It is not only about admitting mistakes but also about testing ideas, noticing what is not working, and being willing to say it out loud while there is still time to adjust. If one person tries something new and says, "We tested this, and it did not work," the whole team gains something. Time is saved. Rework is prevented. Frustration is reduced. Learning moves forward. That is One Team learning: Healthy teams that consistently turn individual moments into shared learning.

Facilitator Note (Opening a Conversation on Learning and Vulnerability)

Use this story (or your own version) to open a learning-focused session with your team.

Ask: "Think of a time when you felt more like Juan—able to acknowledge a mistake and adjust—and a time when you felt more like Cesar—wanting to hide it? What made the difference?"

Invite low-risk sharing as an option: "You can answer based on past experience (not necessarily your current team) or a situation you observed (not necessarily involving you)."

Then ask: "What signals—words, reactions, or routines—tend to make it easier to learn out loud? And what signals tend to shut learning down?"

In the sections that follow, we move from story to practice—how to make learning a deliberate team behavior, not a lucky accident. By the end of this chapter, you will be able to:

1. Recognize how psychological safety shapes people's responses to mistakes—and why those responses matter for team learning.
2. Help your team understand how psychological safety enables learning, especially learning from mistakes, asking for help, and sharing ideas early.
3. Facilitate conversations that make learning intentional,[1] not accidental, and include planning for learning before work begins.

4. Use active learning exercises to surface assumptions, clarify expectations, and practice asking questions in real time.
5. Create space for ideas to be tested, shared, and integrated—so learning becomes part of how the team works.

3.1 Building Together

Even though the broader literature already links psychological safety and learning, teams often struggle to experience that connection in day-to-day work—especially under pressure. To make it tangible, we use an educational game with LEGO® bricks.[2] The activity looks playful on the surface, but it reliably recreates what teams face on real projects: incomplete information, assumptions, time pressure, and the quiet question running in the background—"Should I ask about it, or should I just figure it out?"

This is a two-part game. In Part 1, participants experience the cost of assumptions by building a "dog." In Part 2, they practice safer learning behaviors by building a "duck." Together, the two rounds create a fast, lived experience of what "One Team" feels like in real time: do we struggle in our silos, or do we learn together?

In nearly every session, someone asks afterward, "Why did I not just ask?" And the answer is almost always the same: they were reading the room. When others start building right away, people interpret speed as competence and silence as normal. They do not want to be the one who slows the group down. They do not want to look inexperienced. They do not want to reveal that they are not sure. That is exactly the point—*psychological safety shows up in the micro-moments before anyone speaks.*

> **Facilitator Note**
>
> This activity creates a low-stakes version of real project work.
>
> - Part 1 exposes how quickly assumptions take over when expectations are unclear.
> - Part 2 gives the team a chance to practice learning behaviors that psychological safety enables: asking clarifying questions, checking understanding with others, and sharing what they notice—before it becomes rework.
>
> As you facilitate, focus on what participants notice about their own behavior and what they might do differently in real work.

3.1.1 *Let's Build a Dog*

Open the exercise with this simple instruction:

Build a dog using the pieces you have in your set.

- Give participants a minute to build their dogs using the LEGO pieces provided.[3] You will be surprised by the wonderful designs you get.

Figure 26 The Puppy the Client Was Expecting.

- Thank everyone for participating and ask them to hold up their dogs so others can see what they built.
- Do not volunteer extra details. If someone asks, answer briefly.

This is where learning becomes visible: the word *dog* sounded familiar, the instruction sounded clear enough, but everyone pictured something different. We then show the client's intended outcome (see Figure 26) to highlight how quickly assumptions can fill the gaps when expectations are unclear.

Guide a quick discussion on learning by asking:

Were the client's expectations met?

Most likely, many of the designs in the room did not meet what the client intended. Continue by asking:

Why were the client's expectations not met?

Encourage participants to reflect on the reasons behind the discrepancies (what was expected vs. what was delivered). Common responses include:

- We did not have all the information (e.g., there were no drawings).
- We did not have enough experience (e.g., we had never used LEGO pieces before).
- The design was not ready when we started building.
- The person next to me started building so I just went ahead and did the same.
- We did not ask for what we needed.
- We did not confirm what "done" looks like before starting.

Most of us have been in a classroom where we felt confused or had a question—but because no one else was asking, we stayed quiet—and paid for it later. That same reflex shows up at work: people "read the room," keep questions to themselves, and the cost surfaces later as misalignment and rework.

Facilitator Script

Notice: The instructions did not make it clear that questions were welcome, and many of us assumed we should just figure it out alone. That combination creates a learning barrier, not a capability barrier. That is what happens at work, too. We see others jump into the task right away, and we do not want to look slow or confused.

In one workshop, a superintendent started building immediately. Within seconds, several others followed—almost like a domino effect. Later, when we asked why they did not ask for a picture or a drawing, one participant said, "Everyone looked so sure, I assumed it was me." The room got quiet, because everyone recognized that feeling—not just in training but on the job.

Facilitator Note (Make the "Hidden Rule" Visible)

- Ask the group: What unspoken rules showed up for you? What did you notice happening in the room?
- Common answers: "Do not slow people down," "Do not look inexperienced," "Figure it out alone," "If others started, I'd better keep up."

The Power of Why

This activity is not about letting people fail for the sake of failure. It is about creating a safe moment to study how failure happens before the stakes become real. The most important learning does not come from the wrong dog—it comes from asking why the team ended up there.

When teams stop at "we missed it," they usually stay at the level of reaction. But when they ask why—then why again, and sometimes why again—they begin to move below the surface. What first sounds like a personal problem ("I should have known," "I'm not creative," "I'm bad at this") often turns out to be a system problem: expectations were unclear, assumptions went untested, speed was prioritized over alignment, and no one paused to confirm what success looked like before starting. That shift matters. It moves the conversation away from blame and toward prevention.

Facilitator Script (Exploring the Why)

- "Let's stay with this a little longer. If the client's expectation was missed, why did that happen?"
- "And why did that happen?"
- "What did we assume?"
- "What did we not ask?"
- "What was missing before we started?"
- "What could the client or facilitator have done differently to clarify expectations and make questions easier to ask?"

As the conversation deepens, teams often discover that the real issue was not a lack of effort or intelligence. It was the absence of shared clarity. That realization makes improvement possible. If the problem is "people are not capable," the team gets stuck. If the problem is "we started without enough clarity and no one felt able to slow the room down," then the team has something it can change.

This is exactly the habit we want teams to build in real work. When a handoff fails, when rework appears, when quality drifts, or when a near miss surfaces, the goal is not to rush past it or hide the discomfort. The goal is to pause long enough to understand what happened, learn from it together, and decide what should change.

Facilitator Script (Closing Part 1)

Before we move on, let's name one prevention step you will take next time.

Facilitator Note

Capture responses as: "Before we start, we will ____."
Those prevention moves become the behaviors participants will practice in Part 2.

Common insights teams name at this stage include:

- We need clearer expectations before we begin.
- We should confirm what "good" looks like instead of assuming we all picture the same thing.
- Asking questions early helps prevent rework later.
- When nobody asks, others often assume they should stay quiet too.
- Just because people start quickly does not mean they are clear.
- Learning improves when the team talks about what caused the miss instead of just reacting to the result.

3.1.2 Let's Build a Duck

Continue the exercise by asking team members to take apart what they built in Part 1. Once everyone is ready, give the following instruction:

Build a duck using the pieces you have in your set.

- Give participants a minute to build their ducks.
- In this second round, the "hidden rules" from Part 1 often begin to loosen their grip. People are usually more willing to pause, ask questions, and check assumptions before committing. This is often the turning point in the exercise: participants begin to realize that asking before acting can improve both the process and the result.
- Reinforce the behaviors observed immediately, for example, "Yes—this is what healthy teams do. They clarify before they commit."
- When participants begin asking for more information, acknowledge the questions and provide the Building Instructions Handout. Invite them to continue building.

In one session, a craftworker raised his hand and asked, "Before we start, what should the client's duck look like?" The whole room laughed, not at him but with relief. A single question often unlocks a chain reaction: people begin checking with each other instead of guessing on their own.

Building Instructions Handout[4]

1. Take the red 2×3 brick and use it as the base. This will be the duck's feet.
2. Place the yellow 2×4 brick on top. Leave 2×1 hanging off for the duck's tail.
3. Put the plain yellow 2×2 brick on top of the 2×4, covering the four knobs opposite the tail.
4. Add the yellow 2×1 brick on top, covering the two knobs opposite the tail. This will be the duck's neck.
5. Take the red 2×3 brick and use it as the duck's beak. Place it on top of the duck's neck. Place it in the same orientation as the base, leaving it hanging in the opposite direction from the tail.
6. Take the yellow 2×2 brick with the eyes and place it over the red beak. The eyes should be on either side of the duck, aligned with its neck.

Even with the written instructions, you might get some more questions ("Do you have a drawing?" "Can we see a photo of what it is supposed to look like?"). Let that happen for a few seconds. Then pause and say, "Good catch—we do have a picture of the client's duck. I almost forgot to show it, and you reminded me just in time." Show the client's duck (Figure 27). Then have them continue building with both the written instructions and the visual reference. This is the muscle you are building: ask early, verify together, adjust without blame.

Once time is up, ask participants to stop building and hold up their ducks so others can see the outcome. What you might see:

- Some completed their ducks just as expected.
- Some were still in the building process.
- Some interpreted the written instructions differently, and their ducks did not match the reference.

Figure 27 The Duck the Client Was Expecting.

Guide a quick discussion on learning by asking:

How did your approach change in the second part?

We often see two significant shifts:

- Engagement increases: Participants are more likely to speak up, both to ask clarifying questions and to check assumptions with one another.
- Support becomes natural: Once some participants finish building, they start instinctively coaching their neighbors—"Make sure the tail overhang is on this side," "Flip the 2×2—see how the studs line up?" This behavior is more than kindness; it is a visible signal that learning and progress are shared.

Facilitator Script (Linking Back to Work)

What we just did with LEGO bricks is what happens on projects every day. Expectations are fuzzy, people assume they should already know, and only later do we realize we need more clarity. Psychological safety does not remove complexity—but it makes it safer to ask, "Can we see a picture?" or "Can we walk this in the field together?" **before** we commit.

Facilitator Script (Close Part 2)

What did you do differently this time, and what difference did it make?

Some of the suggestions we often hear include:

- Encouraging team members to voice questions and concerns early: This reduces misunderstandings before they turn into rework, and it makes it normal to say, "I'm not sure how to do this."
- Using visuals: Give the team a shared reference point—"this is what done looks like." A model helps people understand shape, orientation, sequence, and spatial relationships that are hard to capture in writing. This is especially useful when tasks are complex, when people are learning something new, or when language barriers or different experience levels are present.
- Adding a sequence to guide assembly (like an IKEA assembly guide): This makes the process more self-evident. Coding can clarify which piece goes where, in what order, and in what orientation—minimizing mistakes and making assembly easier.
- Providing hands-on training with someone experienced: This gives people an opportunity to practice the task, receive immediate feedback, and troubleshoot together while surfacing hidden assumptions such as, "I thought it meant this."
- Documenting lessons learned and best practices: This helps the team capture what worked, what did not, and what the team would do differently next time so the learning is not lost when teams change, new members join, or similar work occurs elsewhere.

What Success Looks Like

People ask clarifying questions early—before they start building—because they trust that asking is part of doing things right, not a sign of incompetence. You hear participants check assumptions out loud ("Do you read Step 3 the same way?") and name uncertainty without embarrassment ("I'm not sure which side the tail is on—what do you think?"). You also see peer-to-peer support emerge naturally: someone pauses their own build to help a neighbor without taking over, and the receiving person stays engaged rather than shrinking back. Most importantly, when mistakes or deviations from the plan happen, the group stays in learning mode.

This exercise is intentionally simple, so the pattern is easy to see: when people do not feel safe to pause and ask, they rely on assumptions—and assumptions create rework. When the team normalizes asking questions, learning happens earlier, alignment improves, and quality improves. Next, we zoom out from the game and explore how psychological safety shapes learning in healthy teams.

3.2 Unpacking Learning and Psychological Safety

Edmondson's seminal work[5] highlights the critical role of psychological safety in fostering effective learning environments. In construction, learning has to be built into the work. Projects move fast. Conditions change. New materials show up. Plans evolve. Teams assemble and reassemble. And even the most experienced superintendents and project managers still run into situations where the right answer is not obvious on day one.

The question is not whether teams need to learn. The question is whether the environment makes learning possible and expected. In One Team, learning is not a detour from performance—it is how performance stays reliable even when reality changes.

The "I Should Know" Trap

Here is a paradox we see repeatedly: the more experienced or capable someone is perceived to be, the harder it becomes to say, "I do not know." In today's world, competence is often performed under pressure—confidence becomes a social expectation. Once that expectation takes hold, people start protecting their image instead of protecting the work. That is when questions begin to feel like evidence of weakness rather than a natural part of doing the work.

The trap is equating capability with having all the answers. Admitting what they still need to learn can feel incompatible with how competent they are expected to appear. Over time, teams may begin to mistake silence for readiness, confidence for understanding, and the absence of questions for clarity. One project engineer from one of the teams we studied captured this with painful clarity:

> I'd like some guidance. We [everyone at the company] say that we should emphasize quality, but nobody is telling me honestly what to do. People keep on telling me, 'You got to go out there and do it [put quality into practice], you're the one closest to the work on the field, you know how to implement it [the quality plan]' . . . Honestly, no, I don't, I really don't.

This quote reveals a gap between expectation and enablement. The importance of the outcome is clear—quality matters—but the path for achieving it is not.

When people feel they are expected to already know, they stop asking. They stop checking. They stop learning out loud. And One Team begins to break down: knowledge remains siloed, mistakes are repeated, and lessons are relearned the hard way—usually through rework, schedule delays, or strained relationships.

Healthy teams do not confuse accountability with mind-reading. They pair responsibility with the guidance and support people need to succeed. They make the "how" visible: what good looks like, what support exists, who people can turn to, and what questions to ask before work starts. In these teams, questions are not treated as signs of incompetence. They are treated as tools for learning, alignment, and protecting the work.

Gaps to Bridge

Learning does not happen in a neutral environment; it happens within the pressures and unwritten rules of the work. In construction, hierarchy, deeply ingrained norms, and forms of machismo can quietly shape what feels "acceptable" to do or say out loud. If teams are not intentional about making learning part of the work, it can easily get pushed aside—especially in roles where the environment rewards speed above all else. In those settings, staying quiet, just doing the work, and avoiding delay can start to feel like the safer option. Over time, that pattern does not eliminate the need to learn; it simply makes learning harder to do openly. Questions, mistakes, and uncertainty do not disappear—they just become less visible, less discussable, and harder to address together.

One field engineer we interviewed described a consistent difference in how safe it feels to learn across some roles:

> [On the] admin side, we are very good at asking questions and acknowledging when we make a mistake. I'm a big proponent of the only way you learn is by doing something, and if you do it wrong, learning from it and fixing it as a team. I see it differently with our craft, honestly. In a 1 [low psychological safety]-7[high psychological safety] scale, I'd say they are at a 3 or 4. In that aspect, there is much more hesitation there, and I think it is something we still have a lot of work to do.

This gap does not mean craftworkers care less, or that field teams are less capable. It often reflects the conditions of fieldwork. The "cost" is immediate and visible: a wrong install can trigger rework that affects multiple trades, derail a sequence, or create safety exposure. Feedback also tends to happen on the spot—sometimes in a blunt tone—because the work is moving and time is tight.

Power dynamics can also feel sharper in the field. Day-to-day decisions about assignments, overtime, and future opportunities often sit with a small set of supervisors. In that context, staying quiet can feel like self-protection: If I ask too many questions, will I be seen as weak? If I admit a mistake, will I lose the good work? Add long-standing norms that reward toughness and self-reliance, and help-seeking can start to feel like a character flaw instead of a prevention behavior—even though questions are often the fastest route to doing the work right the first time.

Another contributor is the way we develop leaders in the field. Many frontline supervisors—superintendents and foremen—are promoted in part because of their technical expertise and ability to drive production. Yet development in how to lead people may be far less consistent: how to coach without shaming, how to invite voice without losing pace, how to include quieter workers, how to handle conflict, and how to respond when someone says, "I do not understand." Under pressure, even well-intentioned leaders can default to directive communication—short, fast, efficient—and unintentionally send the message that questions are a delay. Over time, voice drops, not because people do not care but because the system teaches them that silence is safer.

And to be clear: none of these reasons justify an environment where people feel unsafe. If anything, the higher stakes of fieldwork make psychological safety more—not less—essential. We watched leaders change the tone in a single week by adding one consistent phrase in huddles: "If you are unsure, that is a signal to ask—not a reason to hide." One superintendent paired that with a simple routine: one "question round" before releasing work. The first few days were quiet. Then a foreman asked a clarifying question that exposed a mismatch between a detail and the material on hand. The team adjusted before installation. No heroics—just a team that made asking normal. Others followed.

Ground It in Reality

Meeting quality expectations is a common struggle across industries. Not because people do not care but because work is complex, fast, and full of handoffs. When team members feel psychologically safe, they are more likely to surface quality concerns early, talk about them directly, and correct them in time—before the issue becomes embedded in the work and more expensive to undo. In other words, psychological safety supports the kind of learning that prevents rework: noticing sooner, saying it out loud, and fixing it at the source instead of later under pressure.

Figure 28 shows which groups first noticed quality issues in two construction projects. In both cases, field personnel identified about half of the issues—52% in Case 1 and 50% in Case 2. That pattern makes sense: craftworkers and their supervisors are the closest to the work, so they are often the first to notice misalignments, missing inputs, buildability problems, and early signs of rework.

The remaining issues were picked up later in the system. The general contractor team identified 28% (Case 1) and 35% (Case 2)—often through inspections, walkdowns, coordination checks, or when downstream work revealed something was not right. Third parties (e.g., architects/owner representatives) identified 20% (Case 1) and 15% (Case 2)—typically at moments when issues are tied to acceptance.

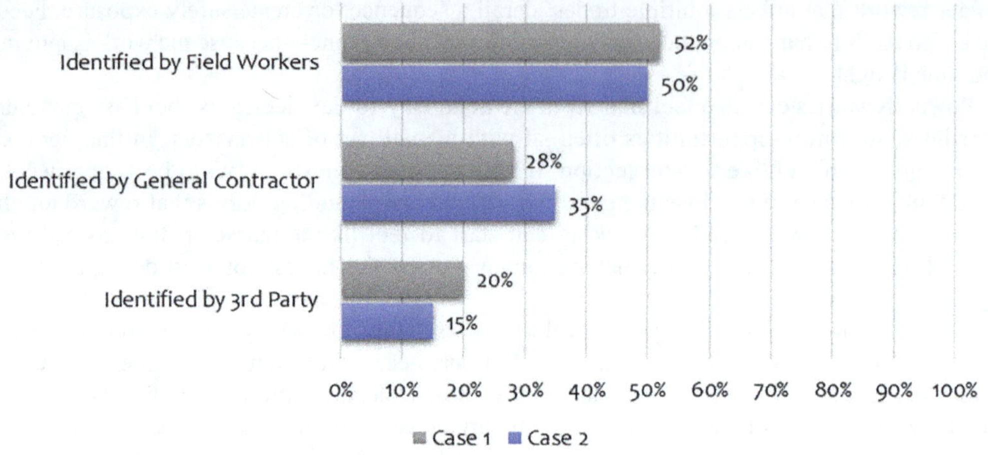

Figure 28 Issues Identified by Layer of Quality Control.

> **Facilitator Script (Link to Your Team's Reality)**
>
> Think about the last defect or instance of rework on your project. Who saw it first? When did the rest of the team hear about it? What got in the way of saying something earlier? (If it feels risky to use a current example, use a past project).

Although field teams identified about half of the documented issues in these two cases, their observations do not automatically become shared learning. When problems stay informal—fixed in the moment without being logged, shared, or translated into prevention—the team loses the chance to (1) spot patterns, (2) adjust upstream processes, and (3) keep the same issue from recurring in the next area, crew, or phase. In other words, the field is doing the detection, but the system is not consistently converting that detection into shared learning. Learning only scales if the people who see the issue feel safe to share it.

Construction projects are notorious for complexity and unpredictability: Unforeseen site conditions, design changes, supply chain disruptions, shifting crews—teams are constantly navigating a moving landscape. In this environment, teams that prioritize learning gain a real advantage. Quality performance is tied to their ability to learn from issues as they arise, converting small signals into better methods, clearer expectations, tighter handoffs, and fewer repeats.

But this is where vulnerability comes in: what if the people who identify the issues do not feel psychologically safe to say what they see?

When asking questions or naming uncertainty carries social risk, the earliest warnings may stay unspoken. A craftworker might notice something is off and quietly "work around it." A foreman might delay raising the issue until it is undeniable. The team does not get the signal when it would have been easiest to act. And the cost is not just the defect itself—it is the lost learning. The same pattern repeats because the team never got the chance to name it, understand it, and build prevention into the system. *Silence does not eliminate risk—it delays and often magnifies it.*

When learning becomes visible—shared, discussed, and turned into prevention—teams do not just fix problems. They get better at preventing them from recurring. This is continuous improvement made real: learning from both successes and failures, adapting as conditions change, and delivering quality more consistently in an industry that rarely stays still.

Team Commitment (Reinforce Early Voice)

- For the next month, every time someone flags a risk or issue early, name the value out loud: "Catching this now saves us from bigger pain later [because . . .]."
- Then close the loop publicly in the next huddle: "Here is what we changed because someone raised the issue early."
- This is how teams learn that speaking up works—and that learning is a contribution.

Learning requires people to feel safe acknowledging when something has gone wrong, but psychological safety does not mean every breakdown should be treated the same way. Teams need to distinguish between mistakes that call for learning and improvement and intentional choices that require accountability. The next section explores how to respond differently to each while protecting both people and standards.

3.3 Distinguishing Mistakes from Deliberate Deviations

In real work, breakdowns are inevitable—especially when conditions shift, handoffs are multidisciplinary and interdependent, and time pressure is real. Breakdowns often come in two forms: an honest miss in a complex system, or a conscious shortcut around a known standard.

So, we need to differentiate them well: *A mistake is part of learning. An intentional deviation is a conscious choice to depart from a known standard or agreement.* Both can lead to harm, but they should not trigger the same response. If teams treat every failure like wrongdoing, people learn to hide problems. If teams excuse a deliberate deviation as "just a mistake," standards erode. Psychological safety requires both: permission to learn and clarity about expectations. Healthy teams respond fairly—curious when it is a miss, firm when it is a choice.

Imagine someone who has never used LEGO bricks before. They follow the instructions carefully—but they still swap a piece, miss a step, or build from an assumption. That is not defiance. That is normal human learning under imperfect conditions. Mistakes often come from skill gaps, unfamiliar tools, unclear instructions, fatigue, or a rushed handoff.

In our LEGO activity, we see this distinction show up in a very human way. In Part 1, when we ask participants to build a dog, some people pause for a split second—then start anyway. Not because they are careless, but because a familiar, unspoken rule kicks in: *I should already know*. With no shared understanding of expectations, everyone fills the gaps with assumptions. And of course, the outcomes do not match—because the expectations were never made visible. And what happens next matters most. When the room responds with curiosity—"What information did we not have?" "What did we assume?" "What kept us from asking?"—the mistake turns into a learning loop instead of a personal failure. And suddenly the "mistake" is no longer evidence that someone is not capable—it is evidence that the process needs review. The team upgrades the process—adding a reference, asking a question sooner, checking alignment before starting.

We have seen the same pattern on jobsites. On one project, a crew installed an element that later had to be reworked—not because anyone was sloppy but because the details changed and the update did not reach the field in time. The craftworkers built exactly what they were told, using the information they had. When the issue surfaced, the response was curiosity: Where did the handoff break? That conversation led to a simple countermeasure: a review huddle before starting the next phase.

Now contrast that with deliberate non-compliance—such as someone repeatedly choosing not to wear safety glasses despite clear expectations and available equipment. That is not a mistake. That is a choice.[6] Intentional deviation involves a conscious disregard for agreed standards and can threaten the team in many ways (e.g., safety, trust, performance). If the team treats that as "just a mistake," it teaches everyone that agreements do not matter. Respect requires addressing this directly and specifically—naming the standard, naming the risk, and naming what must change—so the team stays protected and the person's dignity is preserved. Before treating behavior as an intentional deviation, however, confirm that the standard was clear and understood and that the person had the ability, resources, and reasonable conditions to comply.

Figure 29 summarizes this "fit the response to the situation" idea. When the breakdown is a mistake, the team's job is to stay in learning mode. The focus is not on assigning blame, but on understanding what happened, preventing it from happening again, and strengthening the team's capability. When the breakdown is an intentional choice—a conscious decision to ignore an agreed standard—the response shifts: reinforce the agreement with firm boundaries and name what must change.

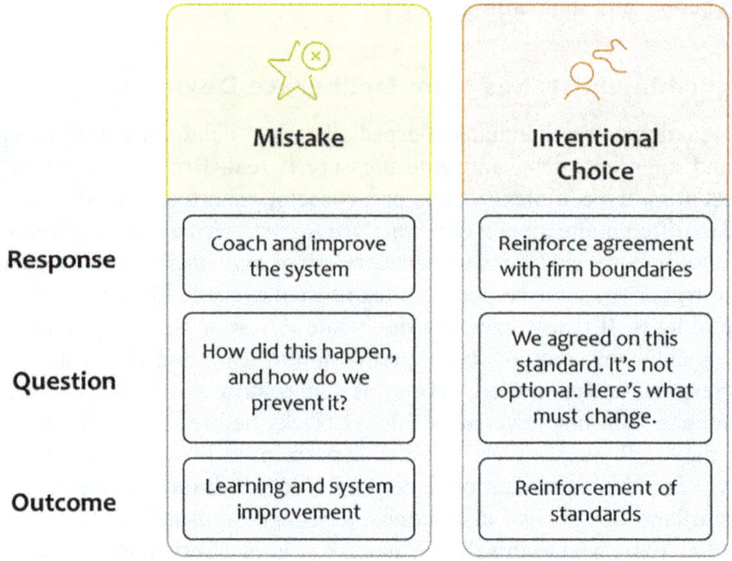

Figure 29 Mistake Versus Intentional Choice—Two Different Responses That Protect One Team.

Facilitator Script (Accountability With Safety)

If this was a mistake, we learn and improve the system. If this was intentional, we address behavior and reinforce standards. Either way, we do not ignore it.

Once a team can tell the difference between learning mistakes and intentional deviations, the next step is building a repeatable response. It is how teams keep standards high without creating fear—and how they turn questions, near misses, uncertainty, and incomplete ideas into prevention and improvement. In One Team, learning is not a personal coping strategy ("I will figure it out")—it is part of thinking as a team ("Let's learn it together"). The next section describes practices to incorporate learning in the flow of work.

3.4 Active Learning in Action

Active learning shows up in the small, everyday moments—when someone pauses to clarify, asks for help, or names what did not go as planned. It is not limited to a formal "lessons learned" meeting after the fact. It is the team choosing to learn in the flow of work, so mistakes turn into prevention rather than repeated rework.

But active learning is not only triggered by breakdowns. It also happens when things are going well—when teams pause to understand what made success possible and what is worth repeating. When work flows, coordination is smooth, and quality holds, a short pause to ask, "What worked, and why?" helps the team capture the behaviors, conditions, and choices worth standardizing—so success becomes repeatable, not accidental.

Why Does This Matter Now?

When active learning is present, teams catch problems earlier, coordinate more smoothly, and prevent repeat rework. They also get better at repeating what works—turning good days into a reliable way of working, not a lucky break. When learning is absent or discouraged, teams pay for it through silence, assumptions, and late discoveries. The cost is rarely one mistake. It is the same mistake repeating in different forms because the team never learned it out loud.

What Does It Look Like in Daily Team Interactions?

By noticing moments of confusion, asking questions, and supporting others when they are unsure, you signal that learning is not just welcome—it is expected. Here are core actions that make learning visible and felt:

Ask for Help Without Shame

- Normalize asking questions as the right thing to do, not a weakness.
- Use a simple help-seeking format: Here is what I tried / What happened / What I need.
- Model and set the tone: "I'm not sure, what am I missing?"
- Encourage mentoring and peer support so people learn both by asking for help and by helping others.
- Make it safe to pause: "Before we start—what is unclear, missing, or assumed?"

Learn Without Blame

- Treat mistakes as information: What is this teaching us?
- Hold "why" conversations that lead to prevention, not punishment.
- Make learning visible: Capture one prevention step and follow through.

- Encourage reflection on both successes and failures—wins teach too.
- For setbacks, run a structured team review: What happened / Why it happened / How we prevent it next time.

Create Feedback Mechanisms That Make Learning Visible

- Build simple, reliable ways for team members to share feedback on processes, procedures, and project outcomes.
- Capture lessons learned in ways the team can reuse—not just discuss—by updating a checklist, adjusting a standard, adding a visual, changing a handoff step, or building the lesson into a pre-task plan or readiness check.

Maintain Accountability While Supporting Learning

- Distinguish mistakes from intentional deviations.
- Respond to mistakes with curiosity + coaching + prevention.
- Respond to intentional deviations with clear accountability and reinforcement of standards.
- Avoid humiliation—accountability can be firm without being demeaning.

Lead Learning *Together*

- Model learning openly: ask questions, seek input, and acknowledge when you do not know.
- Notice and reinforce learning behaviors: when someone asks early, shares a miss, or helps a teammate—name it. You get more of what you reward.

Mistakes will happen, just remember:

Yes, a mistake may look bad, but closing your eyes to it will not make it go away.

Teams that do not learn become dependent on memory, heroics, and repeated recovery. Teams that learn together become more adaptable, more honest, and more capable over time. They do not eliminate uncertainty, but they become better at meeting it—because they have built the habit of asking, checking, sharing, and improving together.

What Does It Look Like at the Organizational Level?

Active learning scales when leaders make it systematic—built into how the organization plans and executes—rather than relying on a few strong personalities to "create a learning culture." Organizations strengthen learning when they build routines that:

- Pull questions forward before work begins through readiness checks, clear expectations, and space to pause and clarify.
- Normalize help-seeking through coaching, mentoring, peer-to-peer checking, and leaders modeling vulnerability and curiosity.
- Close the learning loop by turning lessons learned into changes in how work is done.
- Make learning findable by creating a shared place to capture "what we learned" and "what changed."

Start Small and Start Now

Implement a few deliberate actions that signal, "Questions are welcome here," and practice them consistently. Take a moment to reflect:

- When was the last time someone on your team shared a mistake openly? How was it received?
- What is one barrier to learning in your current team—fear, time pressure, unclear expectations, cultural pressure?
- What is one small change you can make this week to support learning out loud—invite questions earlier, clarify expectations sooner, or share one lesson learned with the prevention steps that will be taken?
- What is one recent "win" your team should study—so you can repeat it on the next phase, crew, or area?

3.5 Highlights

This chapter deepened what it means to be One Team by showing that learning is a team behavior woven into everyday work. When psychological safety is present, teams do not just do the work; they pause, reflect, ask questions, and improve. And they do not learn only when something breaks. They also pause when things go well to understand what made success possible. Learning requires vulnerability—sharing uncertainty, gaps, failures, and half-formed ideas—and psychological safety reduces the interpersonal risk involved.

Key ideas explored:

1. Psychological safety fuels learning: When people are afraid of looking incompetent, they protect themselves. They guess, stay quiet, patch things privately, or avoid asking for help. That slows learning down. When people feel safe, they surface uncertainty earlier, share what did not work, and give the team a chance to respond before the issue grows. The point is not to make mistakes comfortable. The point is to make learning from them possible.
2. High standards and psychological safety belong together: Active learning does not mean excusing everything. Teams need to distinguish mistakes from intentional deviations. Mistakes call for curiosity, coaching, and prevention. Intentional deviations call for accountability. Healthy teams do both. They protect dignity without lowering expectations, and they uphold standards without humiliating people.
3. Healthy teams learn from both failures and successes: It is not enough to ask what went wrong. Teams also need to stop and ask what went well, why it worked, and how to repeat it. Wins teach too. Active learning means treating both setbacks and successes as useful information. That is how teams move beyond reacting to problems and start building stronger ways of working on purpose.
4. Reflection turns experience into prevention: When teams reflect together on why something happened, they move beyond reaction and begin to understand the conditions that shaped the outcome. That reflection helps them surface contributing factors, align on lessons, and build preventive actions.
5. Everyone plays a role: Learning is not just for new team members or training sessions—it is a daily behavior. Leaders who model curiosity help make questions feel legitimate rather than inconvenient. Teammates who offer help, share what they are noticing, and speak honestly

about what did not work make learning more visible and less risky. People who take time to explain, ask one more question, or reflect on what went well help turn individual experience into team knowledge.

Active learning is one of the clearest signs that a team is alive. It shows that people are not just moving work forward—they are paying attention, making sense of what they are seeing, and helping one another get better as they go.

Do not leave learning to chance. Make it normal and expected. Make it safe for people to say, "I'm not sure," "I noticed something," "Let's try this new way," "This did not work," or "This worked really well—let's do it again." The habit of pausing, observing, reflecting, and responding not only improves the work but also strengthens people's connection to one another and their ability to learn and grow together. That is how One Team gets stronger.

In the next chapter, we move from learning together to caring in action. Active caring builds on the mindset of learning by asking a question: now that I notice what is happening, how will I respond? We will explore how active caring turns concern into behavior—how teams notice, respond, and step in for one another in ways that deepen trust and strengthen connection.

Notes

1 Amy Edmondson's (2023) book, *The Right Kind of Wrong*, distinguishes between preventable "basic" failures, multi-cause "complex" failures, and "intelligent" failures that result from thoughtful experiments in new territory. Rather than treating all failure as something to avoid or hide, Edmondson invites teams to design work, so they minimize basic failures, learn from complex failures, and intentionally create space for intelligent failures that move learning forward. This chapter applies that lens in practice, showing how psychological safety allows teams to talk openly about mistakes, surface weak signals early, and turn everyday missteps into shared learning instead of shame or blame.

2 The book *Strategic Play*, by Lloyd Smith et al. (2016), offers a wide range of activities designed to help teams learn through play—surfacing assumptions, strengthening collaboration, and practicing communication and problem-solving in a low-stakes setting. We adapted one of their core game structures for the LEGO exercise in this chapter to make learning (and the role of psychological safety in learning) visible in real time.

3 The set we use for this exercise is the six-piece LEGO Serious Play Duck.

4 These instructions were adapted from the activity "Duck the Instructions" in Lloyd Smith et al. (2016). On projects, "instructions" include drawings, specs, RFIs, mockups, prototypes, pre-install meetings, etc.

5 Edmondson's research shows how psychological safety enables learning behaviors—asking questions, admitting mistakes, seeking help, and speaking up—especially in high-stakes, uncertain work (e.g., Edmondson, 1999, 2018).

6 Be mindful not to jump to conclusions too quickly. What looks like an intentional deviation may in fact be a system issue—for example, a personal protective equipment (PPE) miss may initially be interpreted as an intentional deviation from safety procedures, only for the team to discover that the available safety glasses were badly scratched, fogged immediately, or were not the correct type, making compliance harder than it should have been.

Chapter 4

Let Teams Flourish

Active Caring

Cultivating psychological safety helps create conditions where people feel safer speaking up. Active caring strengthens those conditions through how people look out for, support, and respond to one another. Active caring is what makes "we are in this together" something people can actually experience on the job. It is reflected in the choices we make each day: slowing down to listen, noticing when someone may be struggling rather than looking away, and stepping in to help. In this chapter, we explore how care moves from intention to action—how small, visible behaviors protect each other's work, time, and dignity.

Caring Versus Active Caring

Something I learned early in my work on psychological safety was that caring, although essential, may not be felt by others unless it becomes visible through action. Caring is one of those words that everyone agrees with. No leader would say, "I do not care about my people." Most of us genuinely feel concern when we see someone struggling, overloaded, or heading toward a problem. But my *aha moment* came through my work with teams: what we feel is not always what others experience. *Care that remains an intention may never be visible to the person who needs it.* What people remember is what we do when they are under pressure, when their work is at risk, or when they are learning something new. That is where active caring lives: in specific actions, whether it is providing support, lending a hand, sharing context people need, or simply being there. These actions signal that people are valued and supported and help create the conditions in which they can thrive.

In the world of construction projects, where collaboration among disciplines is paramount, I have had the opportunity to lead and co-lead many craft feedback lunches. Craftworkers are often organized by trade—plumbers, drywallers, electricians—which can limit opportunities to communicate across scopes even though their work is tightly interdependent. Craft feedback lunches bring those perspectives together by giving craftworkers a space to raise concerns, share ideas for improvement, and highlight what is working. To support that exchange, the sessions

DOI: 10.1201/9781003734864-4

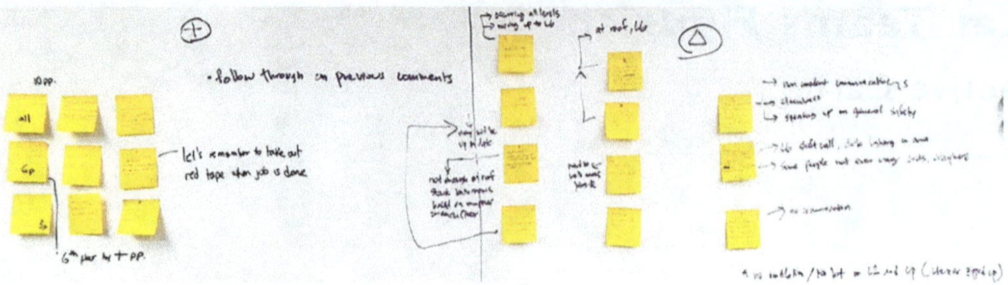

Figure 30 Craft Lunch Feedback Board.

are usually facilitated by a safety manager, project engineer, or project manager. Attendees often include one or two craft representatives per trade, either volunteers or people invited by their foremen. My objective: make it easier—and safer—for the people closest to the work to speak up.

In my early experiences, I observed uneven participation. Some participants engaged actively. Others showed up and left without saying a word. I began to realize that simply inviting feedback was not enough; the way the conversation was structured affected whether people felt able to participate and contribute. To address this, I started giving everyone time to reflect and write their thoughts on sticky notes before opening the group discussion. I then posted the notes on a board (Figure 30) so we could discuss them together. That one design choice did two things at once: it lowered the social risk of speaking up in a group, and it signaled that everyone's input mattered—not just the loudest voices.

Over time, I learned that the design of the conversation was itself an act of care. Dedicating time to individual reflection and brainstorming, and then discussing aggregated group feedback rather than calling on people one by one, helped create a space where more people were willing to participate. Even those who were initially hesitant to provide feedback became more invested in the process as they realized their voices were heard and their input led to visible improvements instead of negative repercussions. The lunches became a way to strengthen the bonds between team members from different trades. This is active caring shown in meeting design: you do not just ask for input—you build a process that protects people while they share their input.

To further increase the impact of these sessions, I started incorporating interactive prompts to gather targeted feedback on specific areas. During one lunch, we expanded the conversation beyond general feedback and explored how the project team was managing quality. I started by asking whether they had all the information needed to install their work (drawings, materials, tools), what quality issues they typically observed, and what actions were taken to prevent rework. As the conversation unfolded, we focused on rework—redoing a portion of work that had already been installed.

I was aware that rework could be a sensitive topic. Rework is not just a metric. It is a lived experience—lost time, physical fatigue, and the feeling that your best efforts had gone to waste. Talking about it asks people to be vulnerable and courageous in admitting that something did not go as planned. Figure 31 reflects craftworkers' experiences with how often they were asked to redo work.

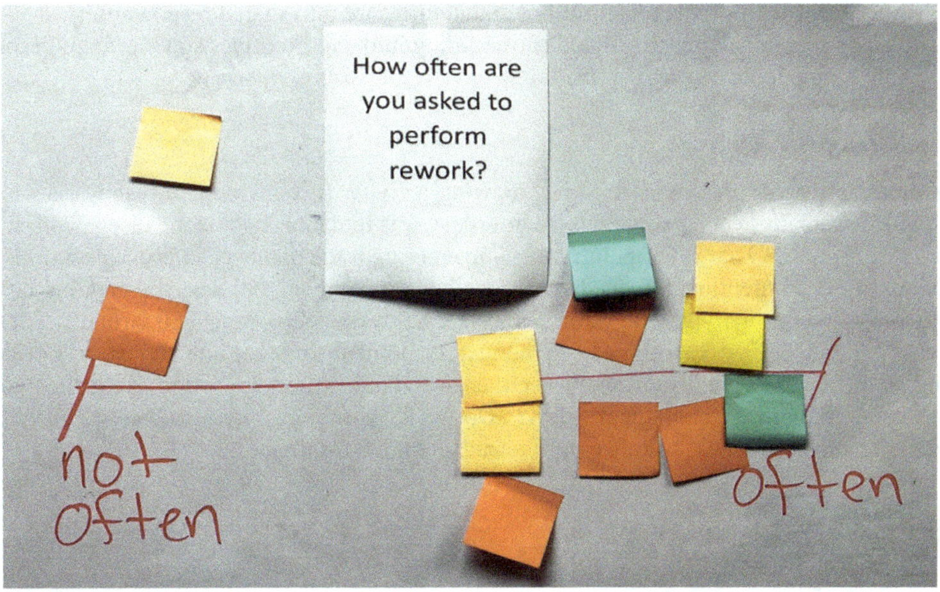

Figure 31 Craftworkers' Perception of Rework Frequency.

Was this a problem with the installation of the work? Was the installation right but the information used was off (e.g., outdated details)? Or was it an owner-driven change? None of the participants knew. And that was a signal. Those who did know (often project managers or superintendents) had not shared that context with the people absorbing the cost in the field. This is where active caring comes in: it is not only understanding that rework is frustrating—it is making sure people have the information they need to learn, adapt, and prevent repeats. When workers are not aware of what happened, they lose the chance to adjust how they build, what they check, or what they ask for next time.

Having to reinstall something that was just installed takes a toll—physically, emotionally, and professionally. So, what would active caring look like in this scenario? It could mean communicating the reason for the rework in plain language and connecting that explanation to prevention. This turns "you messed up" into "here is what drove the change, here is what we are doing to reduce repeats, and here is what we need from you to catch it earlier." By providing that context, care becomes visible and useful. When people have context, they can contribute. When they do not, they just absorb the pain.

Active caring shows people, in visible ways, that they will not be left alone when something is hard, uncertain, or at risk. It turns support from a feeling into an experience. By the end of this chapter, you will be able to:

1. Help your team understand the connection between active caring and psychological safety, and why having one another's backs must be visible, not just assumed.
2. Facilitate conversations and activities that surface how your team currently demonstrates care for one another—and where care needs to be made more tangible.
3. Use a simple drawing game to help people feel (not just hear about) the impact of their actions on others' work.

4. Experiment with rituals of commitment that turn care into shared responsibility.
5. Identify specific actions to embed active caring into daily routines so One Team becomes something people can feel on the job.

4.1 Caring for Others

To explore active caring, we start with a drawing activity. It looks playful—and it is—but it hits home, especially when people realize how easy it is to damage someone else's work while "just doing my job." That is the point: most impact (e.g., trade damage, safety exposure) is not malicious—it is unintentional, rushed, and sometimes "invisible" to the person creating it.

We have used this activity with office teams and field crews, in person and virtually. The setting changes, but similar reactions often emerge: the moment someone alters your work without asking, you feel it—pride, irritation, protectiveness. That emotional reaction opens the door to a conversation about psychological safety: "Do we have enough safety to pause, clarify, and protect each other's work—or do we push ahead and hope for the best?"

Each person plays two roles:

- The Designer (your artistic side).
- The Builder (your production side).

Supplies

- Paper (one sheet per person for the Designer's drawing).
- Markers, pens, and pencils (for both Designer and Builder).
- A timer visible to the group.

4.1.1 The Designer

Purpose

Help participants experience what it feels like to care about something they made—and to see that other people's work deserves the same care.

Facilitator Instructions

1. Everyone plays the role of the Designer in this round.
2. Give each participant a sheet of paper and a marker or pen.
3. Say:

"You are a Designer now. Your job is to draw something that you feel proud of or that brings you joy. It can be a favorite place or a hobby. You have one minute."

Facilitator Safeguard:
Without revealing what will happen in the next round, encourage participants to choose something they care about but that is not sacred or emotionally sensitive.

4. Start the timer (1 minute). Encourage quiet focus.

When the time is up, say:

"Time. Please hold up your drawing so others can see. Take a look around—this is our gallery."

Acknowledge the effort:

"Thank you. These drawings represent something that matters to you. That matters here."

Debrief Prompt

What did you choose to draw—and what does it represent for you?

Facilitator Note

If the room is quiet, you can model vulnerability first: "I drew this because ___. It reminds me that ___. You just created something that matters to you. Notice that feeling. We are going to use it in the next step."

This helps participants connect the care and pride they feel in something they created with the care they bring to their work on a project—even when they do not say it out loud.

Figure 32 shows an example: one participant drew the view he remembered from his window growing up. It is simple on paper, but it carries history—place, identity, and pride.

Figure 32 Sample of Designer's Drawing.

Ask everyone to exchange drawings with another person in the room. Each person should now be holding someone else's drawing.

4.1.2 *The Builder*

Now we switch roles. The same participants become Builders—the production side focused on output. This is where the exercise begins to mirror real work: participants receive someone else's work and are given a production target.

Facilitator Instructions

1. Everyone plays the role of the Builder in this round.
2. Say:

"Now you are a Builder. Your job is to draw circles around the Designer's drawing. Draw as many circles as you can, as tight as possible to the drawing. Remember: you get 'paid' for producing circles. The more circles you draw, the better for you."

3. Set a time limit (1 minute) and start the timer. Encourage them to focus on producing circles.
4. When the time is up, say:

"Stop. Hold the drawing up so we can see it."

5. Ask everyone to look at the drawing they are now holding.

> **Facilitator Note**
>
> You often see two patterns. Some people assume they understand the request and start immediately. Others feel unsure, but when they see others drawing, they follow the group instead of asking. That hesitation—and that "keep up" pressure—is part of what this exercise is designed to surface.

Figure 33 shows a common result: circles tight to the drawing, sometimes crossing lines or covering the part that mattered most to the person who made it. The point is not that the Builder is "bad." It is how easily a focus on production can lead someone to unintentionally damage another person's work. In this exercise, the Builder is responding exactly to what the "system" rewarded: speed and output.

Debrief the activity in two parts.

Part 1: Damage and Rework

> **Discussion Prompts**
>
> - To Designers: Is your drawing just as it was earlier? Any damage, scratches, lines on top? What emotions came up? Are you annoyed? Amused? Protective? Disappointed?
> - To Builders: What did you prioritize? Speed? Accuracy? Protecting the other person's work? What did you not think about in the moment?
> - To the group: Where do we do this at work? Where do we unintentionally reward speed (output) over quality?

Figure 33 Sample of Builder's Circles Around the Designer's Drawing.

Then connect to work:

> In this game, the damage is on paper. On a project, that might mean moving equipment through a finished area, damaging completed work while installing your own scope, occupying space another trade needs, or proceeding before a handoff is coordinated. An action that seems minor from one person's perspective can create rework, delay, or frustration for someone else. Active caring means looking beyond our own task and considering the impact our work has on the people working around us.

Figure 34 zooms in on the result: marks that cut across the drawing, cover important details, and leave visible scratches. Even if you can erase some pencil marks, the work may look "fixed," but time, flow, trust, and the people still take the hit.

Reflection Prompts About Damage

Some of the drawings are damaged to various degrees. Can the damage be fully undone?

Even when you draw in pencil, does erasing the added lines restore the original drawing to exactly how it was?

How is that similar to damaging and then patching someone else's finished work?

What is the cost of the damage here?

What is the "hidden cost" at work? Think about time, morale, willingness to speak up, trust.

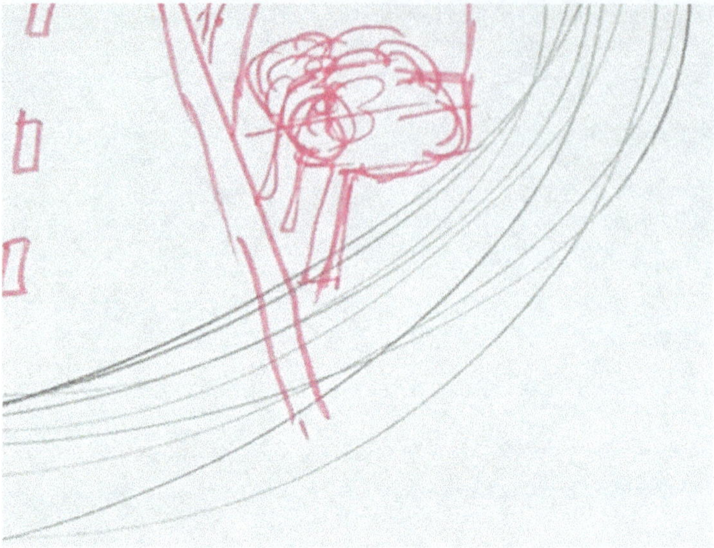

Figure 34 Scratches on Top of the Designer's Drawing.

Part 2: Active Caring Applied

If your drawing was damaged, you may have felt frustration, disappointment, or a quiet sense of "Why did they not watch out for my work?" That reaction matters. It is a low-risk way to feel what trade damage, careless comments, and rushed handoffs can feel like on the receiving end.

Some marks can be erased, but the paper rarely looks the same. On projects, the equivalent might be anything from a scratched finished surface to a lift clipping freshly installed work. You can patch and repaint—but you cannot get back to the original time, the original flow, or the original confidence. Rework has a cost you can measure (hours, material, schedule). It also has a cost you can feel: morale, trust, and willingness to speak up next time.

After participants have reflected on the impact, shift the conversation toward what could have been done differently before the damage occurred.

Discussion Prompts

- We all want to deliver quality to our customer. In this situation, what would active caring have looked like?
- What could the Builder have done before drawing circles?
- What could the Designer or the "customer" have done to make expectations clearer?

Facilitator Script (Make It Explicit)

In the field, it is easy to focus on "getting work done." Active caring asks: "How do we do our job while taking care of the work around us?"

Listen for responses such as:

- Asking a clarifying question: "Before I start, is there any part of the drawing I should be especially careful around?"
- Agreeing on boundaries: "Please keep circles at least this far from the drawing."
- Checking on impact: "How does what I'm about to do affect your work?"
- Slowing down to think about others' work, not just personal targets.

Bridge to Psychological Safety

As you reflect on this activity, notice how many moments come down to one simple choice: pause and clarify, or press ahead and hope for the best. The hesitation you saw—people unsure but staying quiet—often mirrors real project life. People do not always hold back because they do not care. They hold back because they are navigating unspoken pressures: "Do not slow down." "Do not look confused." "Everyone else seems to get it."

Active caring in these scenarios might sound like:

- Before I start, what matters most here?
- Is there anything you want me to protect?
- Show me what good looks like to better understand your expectations.
- Let me repeat what I heard—tell me if I'm missing something.

These are not delays. They are protective moves—small pauses that prevent unwanted consequences. In the field, this might mean asking for a quick demo, referencing a mockup, checking a boundary, or confirming the sequence. In an office context, it might mean clarifying assumptions before work gets handed off, or checking how a change will ripple into someone else's deliverable.

This is where psychological safety becomes practical. People are more likely to ask for clarification, offer a quick check, or raise a concern when they trust they will not be mocked, dismissed, or punished for doing so. When leaders and peers respond well to questions—curiosity instead of impatience, coaching instead of criticism—these protective pauses become the normal way of operating.

Up to this point, we have made a clear distinction: caring is what we feel; active caring is what others can actually experience. Teams often assume these two are the same—until deadlines, tradeoffs, and handoffs reveal the gap. This is where the work of becoming One Team begins: not by saying we have good intentions but by turning care into visible protection—for people and their work.

4.2 From Noticing to Stepping In

The drawing game shows how easy it is to cause unintentional damage. But there is another, quieter pattern we see in teams: people notice a problem, feel concerned, and then walk past it. Figure 35 captures the difference. On the left, someone notices a risky situation—teammates struggling with a heavy box—and thinks, "That looks tough—I hope they do not get hurt," but keeps walking. On the right, that same concern turns into action: they step in and help. The difference is not whether they care. It is whether that care becomes visible support—the kind you can feel and can count on.

Figure 35 Caring Versus Active Caring.

Why do people not step in more often? We argue that psychological safety plays a big role. People worry:

- "Will I look like I'm interfering?"
- "Will they think I'm questioning their competence?"
- "What if they do not want my help or brush me off?"
- "What if I slow them down?"
- "What if I make things worse?"

So, they care—silently. And the team pays the price. The cost is not only the immediate risk. It is the message it sends: "You are on your own." Active caring asks us to cross that line from internal concern to shared action.

Active caring and psychological safety reinforce each other. When care shows up as help, early warnings, and protection of each other's work, people learn that they will not be left alone with problems—and they will not be punished for speaking up. That is how care stops being just a feeling and becomes a visible team habit—one that strengthens safety, performance, and the sense of One Team.

Reflection Activity: Where Are We Not Yet Stepping In?

Caring does not always translate into action. This activity helps the team examine where that gap shows up in everyday work and what may be making it harder for people to step in. The goal is to identify situations where active caring could become more visible and consistent.

How to Run It

1. Introduce the activity:

   "Think about the moments at work when someone (including yourself) could step in to help, warn, support, or protect another person's work—but does not."

2. Ask participants to reflect silently for a minute on these questions:

   - Where do we see people notice something and keep moving?
   - What kinds of situations make it harder to step in here?

3. In pairs, invite each person to share one example from current work or a past project. Encourage examples such as:

   - Someone struggling and no one offering help.
   - A risk noticed but not named.
   - Confusion about the plan, but people staying quiet and pushing ahead anyway.
   - Rework becoming likely, but no one speaking up soon enough to prevent it.

4. Bring the group back together and ask:

   - "What patterns do you notice across these examples?"
   - "What gets in the way of stepping in here?"
   - "What would a small act of active caring look like in those situations?"

5. Close by asking the team to name one behavior they want to practice more consistently, such as checking in sooner, offering help and warning others earlier, or protecting someone's work before a problem grows.

Facilitator Script

"Often, the challenge is not whether people care but whether that care becomes action others can see or feel. This conversation helps us close that gap."

Team Commitment

- For the next four weeks, add a quick closing question to one recurring meeting (huddle, pull-plan, foremen meeting):
  - "Where did someone step in for you this week? Where did you wish someone had?"
- Capture one example each week and thank the people involved by name—specifically naming the action (what they did) and the impact (what it prevented or enabled).

This helps the team notice active caring as it happens and reinforce the behaviors they want to see more often. When teams can point to care ("you jumped in," "you warned us," "you protected our work"), care stops being a private intention and becomes a shared expectation.

In safety, for instance, most people genuinely care; people do not want to see a coworker get hurt. The question is whether that care gets translated into action. Acting on care can look like speaking up when we see unsafe procedures, removing hazards instead of walking past them, stopping a task when something feels off, and showing appreciation when others model safe choices—because that appreciation reinforces the norm: "We step in here."

Table 2 illustrates how active caring can take different forms across safety, quality, planning, and wellbeing. These examples also point to a broader idea: active caring becomes more consistent when teams build it into the way work is planned and coordinated.

Table 2 Examples of Active Caring in a Work Setting

Safety	**Quality**
A crew member notices a coworker about to start a task without required PPE and steps in: "Pause—let's get your face shield." They help locate the right gear so the person can comply without embarrassment. Someone spots a spill/wet surface and acts: they block the area, clean it, and flag the source so it does not keep recurring. During a pre-task brief, a worker shares a near miss from the previous week and explains what would have prevented it. The team adds that prevention step to today's plan before starting work. A foreman hears a rushed instruction that could create exposure and calls a quick reset: "Let's re-walk the lift plan." The pause prevents a shortcut from becoming an incident.	Before handing off work, a craftworker notices a detail that looks "off" and stops to verify—then alerts the next trade so they do not inherit a hidden defect. An installer sees a defect/misalignment early, pauses the work, and pulls in the right support (superintendent/partner trade) to fix at the source instead of letting rework compound downstream. A team member notices that a change in one area could damage finished work in another; they protect the downstream trade by sequencing differently (cover/tape-off, adjust access, change laydown), preventing trade damage. Before starting, someone asks: "What do you need me to protect?"—then confirms plan ("No lifts within X feet," "Cover this surface") before work begins.
Planning	**Wellbeing**
A field engineer notices a missing input (approved detail/material/access) and flags it before crews mobilize—then helps remove the constraint so the field is not impacted. A planner hears "we will figure it out in the field" and pulls the right people together for a 10-minute alignment, so assumptions do not become rework. A team sees a handoff coming that could overload a crew and adjusts plan/sequence early—protecting people from burnout and protecting the schedule from a predictable breakdown. When scope interfaces are unclear, someone steps in to review the contract and confirm ownership—so no one is set up to fail or blamed later for missing work.	A teammate notices someone has been carrying an unsustainable workload and reaches out directly, then helps re-balance tasks. A leader notices a craftworker withdrawing after being corrected in front of others and responds promptly: they follow up one-on-one, clarify expectations without shaming, and re-invite their participation. After a tough week, the team pauses for a quick "pressure check" (Where is the most strain right now?) and makes one concrete adjustment—coverage, pacing, or help—so people are not left to struggle alone. A supervisor shares available support resources (e.g.,leave options) and normalizes using them—so getting help is treated as the right thing to do.

Teams can make active caring easier and more consistent by building it into everyday routines. Before "building time" begins—whether that is literal installation or working on the design phase—teams can schedule time to align: What matters most today? What do we need to protect? Where are we most likely to create rework or risk if we rush?

Healthy teams strengthen this through small check-ins in the flow of work: "Does this make sense?" "What remains unclear before we start or continue?" "What could get damaged if we do not take extra precautions?"

Once teams start acting on care, they may notice a shift—problems surface earlier, handoffs become clearer, and people stop carrying silent frustration alone. One Team builds on consistency and moves from "helping when we can" to protecting each other as a shared standard. In the next section, we turn active caring into a clear team commitment—simple enough to remember, specific enough to practice, and visible enough to hold together.

4.3 Committing to Actively Care

Understanding active caring is one thing. Committing to it together is what makes it durable. In several teams we worked with, a team ritual[1] became a turning point—transforming "we care" from a vague value into a shared promise.

The ritual is simple: *a short pledge and a handshake.*

> "Hi! My name is _____. I promise to take care of your work as if it were my own—and I will let you know when I need your help."

This handshake is more than a greeting. It becomes a shared symbol of cooperation and mutual respect—a way of saying, "I'm in this with you." It gives each person permission to step in when something feels unsafe, off track, or at risk, and makes the commitment public: you are not promising to yourself—you are promising to another person.

> **Facilitator Script**
>
> "This is not just symbolic—it is operational. If I create rework for you, the impact extends beyond the schedule to the whole team. This promise is about protecting each other's work, time, and dignity."

Making the commitment directly to another person makes it tangible. People are not promising to "be nice." They are pledging to protect each other's work, call out risks early, and speak up when something looks off. They are also making it clear that this kind of intervention is welcome—that protecting each other is part of the job, not an intrusion. Over time, those promises change how teams coordinate, how they give feedback, and how they handle mistakes together.

A Shared Promise to Protect

Use this ritual (the spoken promise + the handshake or culturally appropriate equivalent) when you want the team to move from talking about active caring to making it visible and mutual.

Facilitator safeguard:

Make participation voluntary. Physical contact and eye contact should never be mandatory; participants may use a verbal acknowledgment or another mutually agreed gesture.

Step 1—Set the Frame

Explain why the ritual matters: "We have been talking about active caring—how our actions affect each other's work and wellbeing. We are going to close with a commitment to help us make our care visible and shared."

Step 2—Introduce the Pledge

Work with a short, clear pledge so that people can say it with intention rather than just reading it. You can use the one introduced earlier in this section or adapt it to better suit your team. Some alternatives:

> "I commit to take care of your work as if it were my own.
> —I will protect what you have built.
> —I will ask before I act if I am unsure.
> —I will tell you early when I see a risk to our work.
> —I will let you know when I need your help.
> —I will behave as a partner."

Step 3—Pair Up and Exchange the Pledge

1. Ask people to pair up, ideally with someone from another role or company.
2. Invite them to face each other, shake hands (or use a culturally appropriate equivalent), and say the pledge out loud, alternating roles.
3. Encourage attentive presence and a deliberate pace—not a rushed mumble.
4. Ask each pair to name two to three behaviors that would make the pledge visible in daily work. For example:
    - Protecting finished work before staging materials for the next trade.
    - Giving early warning on a scope change.
    - Asking before modifying another person's work.
    - Checking in when someone looks overloaded.
    - Speaking up when a handoff feels incomplete.
5. Have each partner repeat back the behaviors they heard, then write them down so they can follow up.

Step 4—Debrief

- What did it feel like to say—and hear—that pledge?
- What does it mean to you?
- What should we look for in the next few weeks as a sign of progress?

As team members exchange the pledge and a firm handshake, the room often feels different—quieter, more focused. People know this is not just a "feel-good" moment; it is a contract, treat it as such. On projects where we have used this ritual, we saw examples of that commitment showing up in practice: a superintendent talked to a foreman the day before a disruptive activity to ask, "What do you need me to protect tomorrow?" A coordinator paused in a meeting to say, "I gave you my word I would take care of your work like my own—here is how I'm planning to do that this week."

Facilitator Note

Have the leader model the behavior by sharing one moment when they protected someone else's work—or when someone protected theirs. Then name the impact: what it prevented, improved, or made possible. This helps the team see that active caring goes both ways.

Over time, these commitments begin to show up in daily interactions. Feedback stays candid, but it is delivered with a tone that says, "I'm on your side." Ideas move more freely across roles and companies, because the shared commitment helps turn "my job" into "our job." The ritual itself is brief, but the message is long-lasting: we share responsibility not only for the outcomes, but for how we treat one another while we work together to deliver them.

A commitment gives the team language—and permission—to intervene: "I'm stepping in because I'm protecting us." But culture does not change because we say the words once. It changes when those words show up in small, repeatable actions that people can feel in real time: earlier questions, cleaner handoffs, faster close-the-loop updates, and more willingness to ask for help before work breaks. In the next section, we focus on actions teams can use immediately to make active caring part of everyday work not a special effort reserved for "when we have time."

4.4 Active Caring in Action

Caring is the feeling.

Active caring is the behavior. It is care you can point to. It is care you can feel.

Active caring shows up in everyday moments—when someone notices a teammate struggling, protects another person's work, checks in before frustration turns into conflict, or steps in to remove a barrier without being asked. It is not about being "nice." It is the team choosing to make care visible through action, especially when schedules are tight and the work is complex.

Why Does This Matter Now?

When active caring is present, teams coordinate better, recover faster, and prevent small tensions from turning into silence or blame. When caring is absent, or assumed, teams pay for it through missed handoffs, avoidable rework, quality issues, burnout, and people feeling alone in the work. The cost is rarely one harsh moment. It is the accumulation of small moments when people needed support and did not receive it, so they stop asking, stop sharing, and stop trusting.

What Does It Look Like in Daily Team Interactions?

You need attention and follow-through. By noticing impacts, protecting each other's work, and stepping in early, you signal that people matter here—and so does the work handed to each other. Here are core actions that make active caring visible and felt:

Notice and Check In Early

- Look for signals: withdrawal, rushed decisions, frustration, repeated mistakes, missed commitments.
- Use simple check-ins: "You good?" is a start; "What is feeling heavy right now?" is better.
- Ask, "Who might need backup on this?" when planning work.
- Do not wait for someone to "earn" support—offer it when you see a need; give to relieve.
- Follow up after tough moments (a clash, a miss) so people do not carry them alone.

Help Without Taking Over

- Offer support in a way that preserves dignity: "Want a second set of eyes?"
- Ask before jumping in: "Would it help if I . . .?"
- Share resources, templates, and lessons that reduce someone else's burden.
- Mentor in the flow of work—help others learn as they go.

Protect Each Other's Work

- Treat handoffs as relationships, not transactions.
- Check your inputs before sending them downstream.
- Ask: "If I were receiving this, what would I need to succeed?"
- Repair quickly when you create rework for others: acknowledge what happened, learn from it, offer support, and prevent a repeat.

Give and Ask for Feedback

- Address issues with kindness and clarity.
- Active caring is not avoiding accountability; it is delivering it with respect.
- Invite feedback and normalize two-way care.
- Focus on impact and next step: Here is what happened / Here is the impact / Here is what we can do next.

Appreciate and Recognize Out Loud

- Be specific about what you appreciate and why it mattered: "Thanks for checking—that helps us avoid rework."
- Recognize contributions that can easily go unnoticed: stepping in when someone needs help, mentoring someone, or raising a concern early.
- Reinforce what you value: bring examples of active caring into team conversations. For example, in weekly recaps, include a "Care in Action" moment: "Shout-out to the drywall crew for protecting the finished ceiling when opening up that wall. That saved us a day of rework".
- Make recognition something team members give to one another. Create opportunities for people to acknowledge when someone made their work safer, easier, or more successful.

What Does It Look Like at the Organizational Level?

Active caring scales when people turn it from "something good people do" into "how we do work here"—embedding it in expectations for how we hand off work, how we give feedback, how we check in, and how we respond to mistakes, so support and respect are consistent. Organizations strengthen active caring when they build routines that:

- Make care visible and expected (do not just say "we care," but demonstrate it through actions: consistent check-ins, mentoring norms, team agreements).
- Protect downstream work (clear handoff standards, readiness checks, definition of "ready," and quality-at-the-source practices that reduce surprises and protect people's time).
- Create safe feedback loops (regular pulse checks, structured retrospectives, feedback lunches).
- Respond to stress with support (workload balancing, team stability, mental health resources).

Start Small and Start Now

Implement a few deliberate behaviors that signal, "We are here for you," and practice them consistently. Take a moment to reflect:

- What is one way you have seen someone *show* they care—not just say it?
- Where do people quietly carry the load (confusion, stress, rework, conflict avoidance)?
- What is one small act of caring you can practice this week that protects someone else's work—check a handoff, clarify earlier, offer 10 minutes of help, or recognize effort out loud?

Team Commitment: Show Care in Practice

- The 10-second scan: Before leaving an area, take 10 seconds to scan: Did I leave anything that creates risk or rework for someone else?
- The protect-the-work commitment: For the next month, each crew identifies one specific action it will take to protect another trade's work—and share the action taken at the weekly meeting.
- The early-warning promise: "If I see a risk to your work, I will let you know right away."

Write your commitment where the team can see it (on a board, trailer wall, digital channel) and revisit it weekly: Did we do it? Did it help? What needs adjusting? This is how active caring becomes a habit: visible, practiced, and reinforced.

4.5 Highlights

This chapter showed that caring is not enough when it remains invisible. Active caring is what people can actually feel: support that shows up in time, in context, and in ways that protect both the work and the people doing it. When the work is complex and stakes are high, active caring helps keep teams together.

Key ideas explored:

1. Caring versus active caring: Caring begins as a feeling, but active caring is what others experience. It becomes visible when someone shares needed context, designs a safer way for others to give feedback, notices when another person is carrying the cost of a problem, or steps in before strain turns into damage.
2. Small acts of care shape the team environment: Active caring rarely depends on grand gestures. More often, it appears in everyday moments; for example, checking what needs protection before starting work, pausing to clarify, making space for quieter voices, following up after a hard moment, or sharing the reason behind a frustrating change.
3. Care protects both people and performance: Protecting another person's work can prevent damage and rework. Making feedback safer supports learning. Sharing context when something goes wrong can help people adapt instead of absorbing frustration in silence. Checking in early can prevent burnout, missed handoffs, and avoidable mistakes.
4. Psychological safety and active caring reinforce one another: When people know they will not be mocked or punished for offering help, admitting a mistake, or raising a concern, they are more likely to act on their care instead of staying silent.
5. Seeing impact changes behavior: The drawing game makes the dynamic tangible; "just doing my job" can unintentionally damage someone else's work. That felt experience helps participants recognize similar dynamics in trade damage, rushed handoffs, and careless comments—and it opens the door to new norms.
6. Teams can design for active caring: Caring can be built into team routines. The design of a feedback lunch, the wording of a question, the structure of a debrief, the visibility of a commitment, or a simple end-of-day review can all make caring easier to practice.

Healthy teams flourish when people make care visible in the moments that matter most—when someone is uncertain, overloaded, exposed, or affected by another person's actions. Ask yourself: How will people experience my care this week? Will they see it in the way I protect their work, share context, make space, offer help, repair quickly, or follow through?

In the next chapter, we build on this foundation by exploring how teams keep care alive in everyday conversations by pairing speaking up and actively listening. When people trust that they will be met with real attention, they are more likely to to raise concerns, ask questions, and share ideas early.

Let's continue the journey, learning to listen like we mean it, and speaking up with courage.

Note

1 Research on handshaking in negotiations suggests that a handshake can signal cooperative intent and encourage cooperative behavior (Schroeder et al. 2019). Precisely because it is simple, a handshake can carry unusual weight. The pledge ritual in this chapter invites team members to pair a spoken promise with a handshake—or another mutually agreed gesture—so their commitment to protect one another's work becomes visible.

Chapter 5

A Harmonious Blend

Speaking Up and Active Listening

Speaking up is the risk people take to surface concerns, questions, and ideas. Active listening is the responsibility the team takes to receive that risk with attention, curiosity, and follow-through. When one is missing, the other fades. Speaking up and listening are a paired discipline: they must be practiced together. One creates the opening; the other shows it is worth stepping into. When teams treat listening as a deliberate action—they replace guessing with clarity, turn "why bother" into "it is worth saying."

A Blend to Thrive

Some of the most important moments in a team's life happen in a simple exchange: one person takes the risk to speak, and the room decides—through its response—whether taking that risk was worth it. You can invite people to speak all day—but if the room is not prepared to really listen, speaking up eventually disappears. You cannot ask people to take a risk and then respond in ways that make them regret it. That lesson became real for me during the feedback sessions I hosted with craftworkers on a construction project. These sessions were designed to provide a space where workers could voice their thoughts and provide feedback on what was going well—and what needed improvement. Figure 36 shows one of these moments in practice: craftworkers gathered together to surface concerns, hear one another's perspectives, and identify ideas the team could use to improve.

At first, the room was not hostile—it was guarded. Most participants stayed in "safe" territory: compliments, generalities, and silence. The appreciation was real—but so was the gap. We were hearing what was easy to say, but improvement also requires people to name what could be better—early and without fear. When feedback stays filtered, learning gets delayed—and delayed learning shows up as late surprises, frustration, and rework.

That pattern held until one person finally voiced a frustration that may have been shared by others in the room: "Why bother speaking up if nothing is going to change?"

I had seen teams reach this point before, but hearing it stated plainly, in a setting created to listen to people's feedback, made the dynamic impossible to ignore. In Chapter 1, we talked about futility: the belief that speaking up will not lead anywhere.

My *aha moment* came right there: People were not deciding whether they had something to say; they were deciding whether it was worth saying. When voice has a history of going nowhere, silence becomes rational. They were doing the math and deciding that the risk was not worth the return. And once that belief takes hold, "encouraging participation" is not enough. *People do not need a louder invitation; they need evidence that their voice will be received with care and turned into something real.*

DOI: 10.1201/9781003734864-5

Figure 36 Craftworkers' Feedback Session.

And "listening" is more than staying quiet while someone else speaks. It means treating what they share as valuable information—not as an interruption, a complaint, or a threat. It means responding in a way that makes space for the person to clarify, elaborate, and be understood.

Later, I learned that the literature describes this kind of listening as active listening. This listening goes beyond simply hearing (receiving words)—it is the deliberate work of trying to understand. It requires a genuine desire to understand, along with attention, engagement, and empathy. It shows up in what you do while someone is speaking: the questions you ask, the meaning you reflect back, and the emotional signals you acknowledge without rushing to fix them.

Understanding what was happening in the room, I adopted the following strategies:

- Make the "why speaking up matters" explicit: I learned not to assume people already know this. In different seasons of my own career, I have felt both: speaking up can feel risky, and speaking up can feel pointless. So, I began each session by explaining how speaking up can protect people and strengthen the team.
- Practice active listening out loud: I slowed the pace of the conversation and made listening visible by asking follow-up questions, paraphrasing what I heard, checking that I understood what they meant, and thanking the person for the risk they took in sharing their ideas. I wanted the group to see what "receiving feedback with care" actually looked like.
- Close the loop with action: I started coming back to the team with examples: "Here is what we changed because you raised that," or "Here is what we tried," or "Here is why we cannot change that yet—and what we can do instead." I learned that *the worst response to feedback is not a "no." It is silence.*

Over time, the blend started to work in the way it is supposed to. When craftworkers saw that feedback was met with respect and care—and that the team did not respond to honesty with defensiveness—they began to offer more specific input. The conversation moved from "everything is fine" to "here is what is making the work harder than it needs to be." And once that happened, the sessions became more focused on learning and improving together—because speaking up surfaced reality, and active listening turned that reality into something the team could use.

In this chapter, we build practical capability in both directions: how to voice concerns and questions clearly, and how to receive those concerns in a way that makes the next person more willing to speak. One Team is built by everyday interactions in which people feel heard, respected, and confident that their input will lead to learning and action. By the end of this chapter, you will be able to:

1. Explain why speaking up and active listening must be practiced together—and how each one reinforces (or undermines) the other.
2. Recognize common breakdowns that silence teams (fear and futility), and identify what those breakdowns look like in everyday interactions.
3. Use a drawing activity to help teams experience different levels of listening and the impact those levels have on clarity, trust, and willingness to speak.
4. Practice active listening behaviors—paraphrasing, asking clarifying questions, acknowledging emotion without rushing to "fix" it, and closing the loop—so people feel safe to contribute.
5. Design small team routines that reduce guessing, improve handoffs, and make it easier to raise concerns early.

5.1 Exploring Levels of Listening

To make active listening tangible, we use a drawing activity. It is simple on purpose. The task is low-stakes, but the dynamics are real: split attention, assumptions, frustration, and the temptation to blame the other person instead of improving the interaction. This exercise helps teams "see" listening as behavior that protects handoffs, decisions, and relationships.

Facilitator Note (What to Watch For)

Most people are not ignoring others on purpose—they are too busy multitasking. They are hearing words while their brain is already deciding, judging, or preparing a reply. When the Listener does not slow down to verify meaning, the Speaker stops taking the risk to share or clarify. That is the moment speaking up starts to fade—because the Speaker learns, "I'm not really being received."

Set-Up

1. Pair up the participants (the Speaker and the Listener).
2. The Speaker receives an image (only they can see it).
3. The Listener has blank paper and draws the image based on the Speaker's instructions.
4. Run three rounds with the same partners. Each round changes the quality of listening.

5. Do not share or compare drawings between rounds. Keep each round's drawing hidden until after Round 3 so participants can compare all three at once.
6. Reset between rounds: new sheet each round, no erasing old work, and no peeking at the image.

5.1.1 Disengaged Listening

Round 1 simulates what happens when attention is split. The "listener" hears words but does not work to understand their meaning. This is the kind of listening that quietly teaches futility: "Why bother?"

Facilitator Script (Round 1)

- To the Speaker:
    - Describe the image. Keep going even if you notice your partner is not following.
- To the Listener:
    - During this round, act distracted. Look away. Check the time. Give minimal responses.
    - Do not ask clarifying questions.
- Time: 2 minutes.

Debrief Prompts

- To the Speaker:
    - What did it feel like to give instructions when you were not getting real attention?
- To the Listener:
    - What did you notice about your ability to understand the instructions?
    - How confident were you about your final deliverable?
- To both:
    - Where does Round 1 listening show up in your team—especially when schedules are tight or stress is high?
    - What can the team do better next time?

Facilitator Note (What This Round Reveals)

Disengaged listening does not just lower accuracy—it changes the relationship. When the listener is distracted, the speaker often works harder to be understood: repeating, simplifying, over-explaining, or giving up.

Disengaged listening also creates room for assumptions. Without clarification, the listener fills gaps with their own mental model, and the speaker assumes the message landed. That gap is where mistakes happen—quietly. On real projects, it often looks like people proceeding to install work with an incomplete understanding because they do not feel they can slow things down, ask again, or interrupt the flow.

Round 1 listening often shows up as people being too busy to pause—multitasking in meetings, checking phones, rushing handoffs, half-responding during field coordination.

5.1.2 *Partially Engaged Listening*

Round 2 reflects what many teams consider "normal" listening: polite, but still shallow. The listener seems to be present but not actively trying to understand. They may nod, say "yeah," or jump to conclusions without verifying. This is the most dangerous round on real projects because it can create the appearance of alignment without confirming shared understanding.

Facilitator Script (Round 2)

- To the Speaker:
  - Keep describing. Notice when you start to simplify because you assume they "should get it."
- To the Listener:
  - Look engaged, but do not verify. You can say "okay" and "got it," but avoid paraphrasing or checking assumptions. Only Yes/No questions are allowed.
- Time: 2 minutes.

Debrief Prompts

- What improved?
- What still broke down?
- What is the cost of "polite" misunderstanding on a project?
- Where does Round 2 listening show up in your team?
- What can we do better next time?

Facilitator Note (What Improves—And What Still Breaks Down)

Partial engagement often creates the illusion of alignment. People nod, say "yes," or ask quick check-the-box questions, and everyone feels like they are moving forward. But the deeper meaning is still unverified. The speaker may withhold details to avoid overwhelming; the listener may avoid "obvious" questions to protect their image. Psychological safety matters here: when it feels risky to ask, people trade clarity for speed.

This is also where narrow questions restrict information. If the listener asks only closed or leading questions, the speaker responds inside that narrow frame—leaving key context unspoken. In project settings, Round 2 listening is a major driver of rework: teams are not careless; they are operating on a partially shared understanding.

Round 2 listening hides behind phrases like "I think I understand." Treat those phrases as a cue to verify: "What did you hear?" "What is still unclear?" "What assumptions are we making?" Clarity is not slowing the work down; it is avoiding surprises downstream.

5.1.3 Fully Engaged Listening

Round 3 reflects active listening in practice. The listener's job is to build shared understanding with the speaker. This is where speaking up becomes more likely because the speaker receives a clear signal: "Your voice matters, and I'm working to get it right."

Facilitator Script (Round 3)

- To the Speaker:
    - Keep describing. Speak at a manageable pace, pause for questions, acknowledge confusion without criticism, and confirm features before continuing.
- To the Listener:
    - Use active listening. Ask clarifying questions. Paraphrase what you heard. Confirm details before drawing.
- Optional phrases to connect:
    - "Let me repeat that back to make sure I'm tracking."
    - "What do you mean by . . .?"
    - "What is the most important feature I should get right first?"
- Pay attention to your body language (e.g., eye contact, nodding, posture, hand position, pace).
- Time: 2 minutes.

Debrief Prompts

- What changed in the result?
- How did you feel in this round?
- What changed in the relationship?

Facilitator Note

Fully engaged listening turns a one-way explanation into a shared build. The listener is no longer simply receiving instructions—they are co-creating clarity through paraphrasing, questions, and confirmation. Figure 37 shows what teams typically see when they compare drawings across rounds: the early drawings reflect the listener's assumptions, while Round 3 is often closer to the original because meaning was verified before action.

This improvement in outcomes matters—but so does what happens in the interaction: when people feel listened to, they are more likely to share details, acknowledge uncertainty, and correct misunderstandings early.

After Round 3, have the pairs compare drawings across all three rounds. The side-by-side contrast helps participants see how listening affects the outcome. Round 3 is not "extra communication." It is the minimum standard for high-stakes handoffs, complex coordination, and decisions that will be hard to undo.

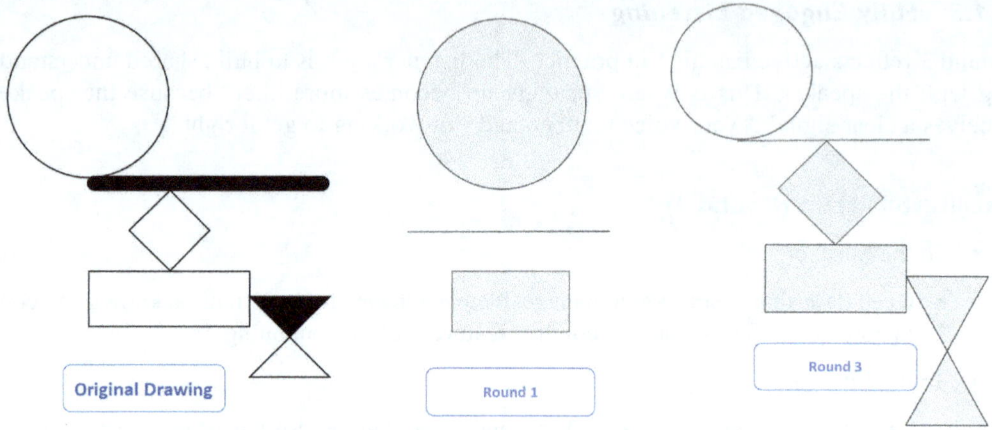

Figure 37 A Snapshot of Listening Quality and Outcomes.

Facilitator Note (What This Round Makes Possible)

Active listening changes the speaker's experience: feeling heard gives them space to think, clarify their ideas, and express what they mean more fully—and can make speaking up more likely next time. Open-ended questions are a key tool here. They invite richer responses, help the speaker explore and articulate what they mean (not just what they said), and give the listener what they need to close gaps.

Facilitator Script (Closing)

"Where in your team do you need Round 3 listening the most—handoffs, pre-task planning, design clarifications, constraint removal, or feedback conversations?"

Team Commitment

Before moving on, practice one verification routine: paraphrase ("Here is what I heard . . ."), clarify what remains uncertain ("When you say X, do you mean . . .?"), and confirm the next step ("So you want me to . . . by when?").

After teams experience these three listening modes, the pattern becomes easier to see: how people respond affects whether others keep speaking up. That is why "encouraging people to speak up" is not enough. If you want voice, you have to shape the listening environment that makes voice feel safe, worthwhile, and effective—especially when what is being raised is inconvenient, uncertain, or disruptive. In the next section, we name what this game makes visible: how common listening patterns shape psychological safety over time, and how the response—especially when the work gets messy—is often what keeps voice alive or quietly shuts it down.

5.2 Promoting Voice Through Listening

Listening is a social signal. The way people respond while someone is speaking up, explaining something, raising a concern, or offering input teaches others what is welcome in the team. People do not just hear what is said—they learn what it costs to say it.

Figure 38 shows what some listening patterns communicate over time: the message people take away, the level of psychological safety that tends to follow, and the kind of voice behavior a team can expect.

When disengaged listening becomes common—people look away, multitask, or respond with minimal attention—the message received is dismissal. Even if no one says it out loud, the signal lands: "You are not a priority." Here, the social risk of speaking up feels high, and voice becomes rare. People save concerns for later, soften them, or stop sharing them altogether.

When limited engagement becomes the default—polite nods, a quick "got it," and narrow check-ins—the message received is speed over understanding. It can look efficient but often produces surface alignment and hidden assumptions. Here, people speak up, but cautiously. Concerns get filtered, details get withheld, and truth arrives late—often after work has already moved forward. This is where teams feel busy and still miss each other.

When active listening becomes the norm—questions that clarify, paraphrasing to confirm meaning, and a genuine effort to understand—the message received is respect and shared ownership. The signal lands as: "Your voice matters, and we will handle this together." Here, the

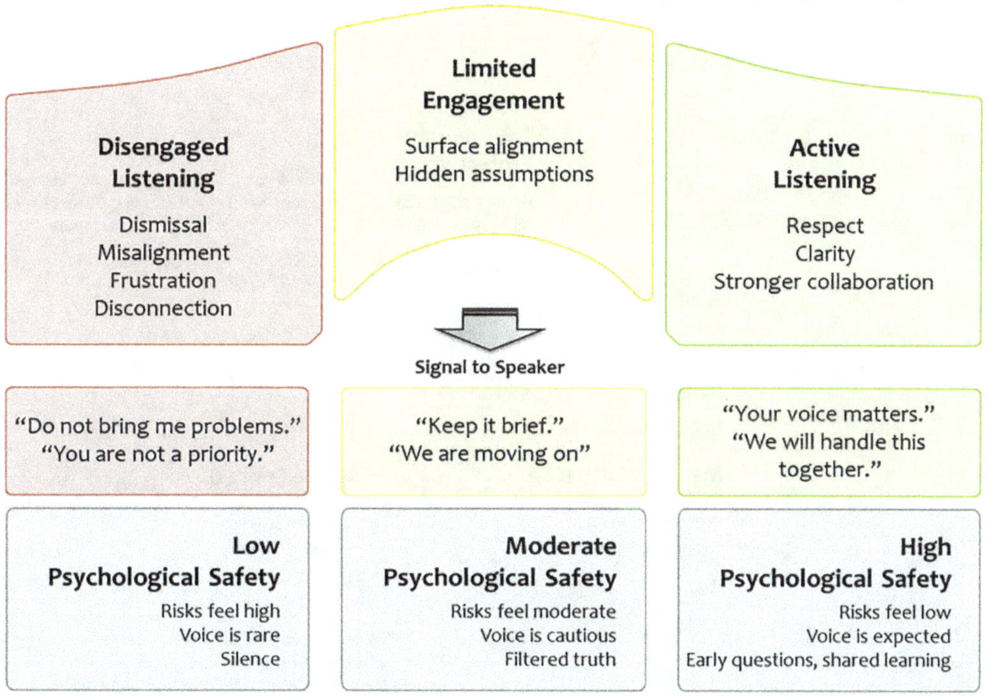

Figure 38 How Listening Signals Change the Social Risk of Speaking Up.

social risk of speaking up feels lower, and questions show up earlier, when problems are still small and easier to solve.

Ask yourself:

"What will you do differently in the way you listen so the next person leaves knowing their voice mattered—and feels safer speaking up again?"

Listening When the Work Gets Messy

Listening becomes especially critical when the work gets disrupted—a constraint shows up late, a quality risk is raised, a plan is challenged, a deadline is threatened. These are the moments that decide whether a team stays healthy under pressure—or starts protecting itself through silence. Those moments are where teams either learn "it is safe to surface reality here" or learn "keep it to yourself next time."

Figure 39 highlights some elements that help teams respond during disruptions.

Protect Voice

The first step is to respond in a way that does not make the person regret speaking up. This does not require agreement with the concern—only respect for the act of raising it. Examples:

- "Thank you for flagging that. I'm glad it is coming up now."
- "I hear the concern. Let's slow down for a minute and look at it."

Figure 39 Listening Strategies to Protect Voice During Disruptions.

- "Good catch bringing this forward."
- "Before we move on—let's make sure we understand what you are seeing."

Explore Context

Once voice is protected, the next step is to understand what the person is seeing. This is where open-ended questions matter, because they invite details. Examples:

- "Walk us through what you are seeing. What is driving the risk?"
- "What changed? What is different than what we assumed?"
- "What is the constraint here—information, sequence, capacity, approvals, access?"
- "Let me repeat what I'm hearing—tell me if I'm missing something . . ."

Make It Worth It

This is the moment that shows whether speaking up leads to a constructive response. Even when the solution is constrained, the team can still create a clear next step and close the loop. Examples:

- "What support would help most right now?"
- "Before we move on, let's agree on the next step, an owner, and when we will revisit."
- "Here is what we are doing next, and here is when we will check back."

Over time, these responses become a pattern the team can count on. Disruptions still happen, but people stop treating them like personal threats. They become shared problems—surfaced earlier, handled with more clarity, and resolved with less rework and less blame. That predictability is what keeps voice alive.

Even when people feel safe to speak and their input is received with respect, misalignment can still occur if assumptions remain unspoken or shared understanding is not confirmed.

5.3 Aligning Expectations

Think about this request: "Can you pack an apple for my lunch?" One person pictures a whole red apple. Another pictures a sliced green apple. Neither interpretation is unreasonable. The miss happens when the expectation stays implicit—inside someone's head. This is often how most misalignment starts: not with bad intent but with different assumptions about the desired outcome.

Figure 40 illustrates the problem: sometimes a request sounds obvious, so the conversation stops too soon. At other times, the request feels only partly clear—but the person receiving it hesitates to ask a question that seems "too basic," worries about slowing things down, or assumes they should already know. In both cases, people leave the exchange with different internal definitions of success—or with unspoken uncertainty they fill in on their own. The result is predictable: both people believe they understood enough to proceed, and the mismatch only shows up later, when it costs more.

Mental models are where expectations live before they are made explicit. These are internal images and interpretations that people carry about what a request, instruction, or situation means—often without realizing they are assumptions. On teams, the same pattern shows up in higher-stakes ways: "finish this right away," "do it right," "ASAP." Those phrases can sound clear—and still

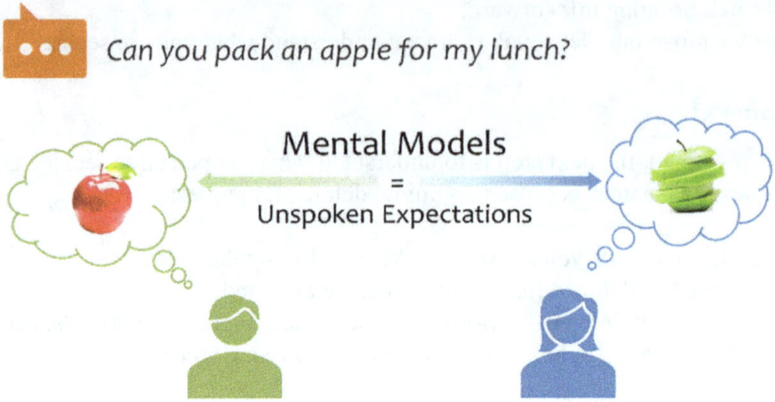

Figure 40 Expectations as Mental Models.

produce different outcomes—because each person is filling in the blanks with their own mental model. When expectations remain implicit, people guess. And guessing is where confusion, rework, and frustration start.

A mental model is built from someone's:

- Past experience ("this is how it is usually done").
- Preferences ("this is what 'good' looks like to me").
- Role and training (field vs. office, designer vs. builder).
- Context and constraints (schedule pressure, risk, quality standard).
- Unspoken definitions ("ready," "done," "acceptable," "urgent").
- Frame of reference (culture, background, upbringing, education).

That is the mechanism behind so much everyday friction on teams. We assume we know what the other person means. But unless we do the work of checking, we can execute competently and still miss the mark. In other words, you can deliver exactly what you thought was asked for—and still fail to deliver what the other person actually wanted.

Aligning expectations means making the invisible visible. It means turning the mental model into shared language before action happens. This is also where psychological safety becomes essential: people need to feel safe to ask, "What do you mean by that?" and safe to clarify expectations without being perceived as controlling or incompetent. When teams normalize that checking step, they reduce guessing, prevent avoidable missteps, and protect trust—because the handoff is built on shared meaning, not assumed meaning.

Figure 41 breaks this kind of exchange into four practical conversations that help teams move from raising something important to getting aligned on what to do next. The sequence begins with speaking up clearly—making a concern, need, question, or idea explicit instead of leaving it unspoken. It then moves to listening to understand, where the other person receives that input with attention and curiosity rather than interruption or defensiveness. Next comes checking meaning: testing assumptions, clarifying what matters, and making understanding visible before people act on incomplete interpretations. Finally, the conversation moves to aligning and acting—summarizing what was heard, confirming next steps, assigning ownership and closing the loop. Together, these behaviors help teams replace guessing with clarity and alignment.

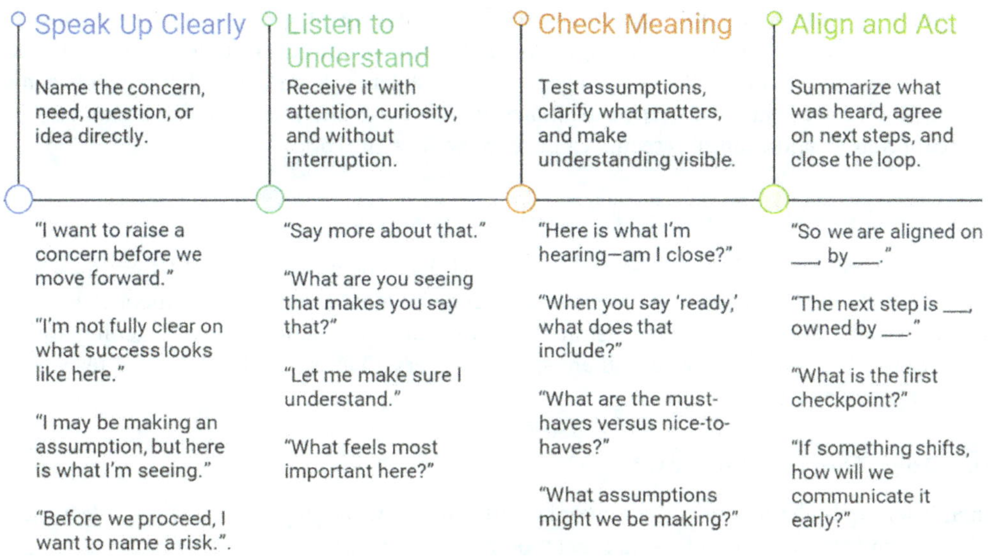

Figure 41 A Practical Conversation Pattern for Alignment.

In practice, it often starts with a small pause before acting: "I want to make sure I understand what you need from me." In psychologically safe teams, that pause is welcomed. It is not treated as slowing down the work; it is treated as a normal step in protecting the work. When teams practice this consistently, they are more likely to catch differences in understanding before those differences become problems.

Facilitator Note

Give participants a chance to practice these skills before they need to use them in the moment. Pair them up and ask one person to share a real work situation from the past—ideally one that is no longer active—where an expectation, request, or decision needed to be understood clearly.

The listener's role is not to solve the situation or give advice. Their role is to listen, ask questions, and confirm what they understand. After a few minutes, switch roles so both people can practice. Encourage them to use prompts such as:

- Clarify: "When you say ___, what do you mean?"
- Reflect: "So you want ___, by ___, and it needs to include ___."
- Confirm: "Is that right? Anything else that matters?"

Debrief:

- What did the listener do that helped—or did not help—you clarify what you meant?
- What was difficult about checking or confirming understanding?
- What could you use from this practice in a real conversation?

Remember, *misalignment rarely announces itself.* It shows up later—as rework, side conversations, or that quiet frustration of "I thought you meant . . ." Alignment routines stick when teams build them into the rhythm—the quick question before a handoff, the check that prevents a miss, the close-the-loop update that keeps trust intact. In the next section, we turn those moments into practical prompts and examples teams can use in the flow of work.

5.4 Speaking Up and Active Listening in Action

Speaking up and active listening are not separate skills to be mastered in isolation; they move together. When people take the risk to share a concern, an idea, or a mistake, someone else either receives it with attention—or with distraction, impatience, or silence. Active listening signals: I'm here, I'm listening, and what you are saying matters. Over time, that response teaches the team that speaking up is worth it.

Why Does This Matter Now?

When listening is shallow or rushed, people start filtering what they say. They share less, delay bad news, and stop offering ideas that feel "too risky." Conversations become one-way updates instead of real dialogue. On the other hand, when people feel truly heard, they are more willing to surface problems early, admit uncertainty, and co-create solutions. Listening becomes a way of building psychological safety in real time.

What Does It Look Like in Daily Team Interactions?

You do not need extra meetings to practice this. What changes is the quality of conversations that already exist. Here are core actions that make speaking up and active listening visible and felt:

Make Space Before You Listen

- Check your capacity: if you are truly rushed, say so and propose a better time: "I want to give this my full attention—can we talk at 2:30?"
- Minimize distractions: put your phone down, close your laptop, no multitasking.
- Signal your presence: face the person, maintain appropriate eye contact, and use body language that shows attention.

Listen With Curiosity, Not Certainty

- Aim to understand, not to fix. Resist the impulse to jump to solutions or judgments.
- Notice your internal monologue: are you preparing your defense, rehearsing your reply, or truly taking in their words? Return to listening mode.
- Ask yourself: "What am I missing? What might they be seeing that I do not?"
- Use simple, open questions: "Say more about that . . ." "What worries you most here?" "What feels unclear?"

Check That You Understood What Was Said

- Paraphrase: "Do I understand correctly that you are concerned about . . .?"
- Name both content and impact when appropriate: "If I understand correctly, the schedule change means your crew will need to resequence the work. Is that right?"
- Invite feedback: "What did I miss or get wrong?"
- Summarize before moving on: "So far I'm hearing three things . . ."

Respond in Ways That Support Speaking Up

- Start by acknowledging what was raised: "Thanks for bringing this up."
- Separate the idea from the person: Challenge assumptions without dismissing the contributor.
- Resist the "my turn" reflex: Stay with their story.
- If you disagree, stay curious: "I see it differently; can we walk through your view step by step?"
- Avoid quick fixes that skip understanding. If you need time to investigate, say so: "I hear you. Let me look into this and I will come back to you by . . ."

Pay Attention to Verbal and Nonverbal Cues

- Listen for what is *not* being said: long pauses, avoidance, sudden changes in tone, or vague language around sensitive topics.
- Notice possible signs of guardedness—crossed arms, forced laughter, a frequent "it is fine"—and gently invite more input to unpack.
- In group settings, watch who speaks easily and who rarely gets airtime. Use your role to draw in quieter voices without putting them on the spot.

Document, Follow Up, and Build Routines

- Close the loop: if someone speaks up about an issue, let them know what happened next—even if the answer is, "We are still working on it."
- Make next steps visible: "Here is what we are doing, who owns it, and when we will revisit."
- Build small listening routines into existing meetings: a check-in round, or a closing question such as, "What did we hear today that we need to act on?"

Speaking up and active listening are built on moments that repeat: choosing to pause instead of rushing to the next task, asking one more question instead of assuming you already know, staying with someone's words instead of half-listening while your mind runs ahead. Over time, they tell people, "Your perspective belongs here. When you have something to say, we will make room for it."

What Does It Look Like at the Organizational Level?

Speaking up and active listening take root when they become more than the habits of a few thoughtful individuals and become part of how the whole organization operates. That requires more than encouragement; it calls for shared routines, clear expectations, and simple structures that make listening visible and expected in the way meetings run, issues are surfaced, and decisions are made. Organizations strengthen active listening when they:

- Design meetings for voice (use structured rounds so different roles can speak without being interrupted, make time for questions before decisions are finalized, build in reflection time, and pause before closing to ask: "What did we hear? What did we miss?").
- Set clear norms for how team members interact (e.g., no talking over others, one conversation at a time, paraphrase before disagreeing).
- Create safe and accessible feedback loops (use regular pulse checks and retrospectives, offer different channels for voice).

- Invest in listening skills (provide coaching and training on listening, not just presentation skills, integrate listening behaviors into leadership expectations and development plans).
- Make listening visible and valued (recognize people who surface missing perspectives, ask follow-up questions, and ensure concerns raised are acknowledged and addressed).

Start Small and Start Now

Pick one place this week where listening and speaking up will be more intentional: a one-on-one, a huddle, a coordination meeting, a crucial conversation. Take a moment to reflect:

- Think of a recent conversation: did you feel truly listened to—or just heard? What made the difference?
- What is one small shift you can make this week that would make voice feel safer and easier?

5.5 Highlights

This chapter reminded us that speaking up and listening are a pair. Neither, on its own, can sustain psychological safety. A team can invite "open and honest dialogue," but if voice lands in rushed meetings or unanswered follow-ups, people learn that their voice does not really make a difference.

Key ideas explored:

1. Speaking up is shaped by a rapid, often unconscious calculation: People often decide whether to speak based on the perceived risk (fear) and the expected impact (futility). When the risk feels high or the impact feels low, silence becomes a rational response. That is why healthy teams do not judge silence too quickly; they get curious about the conditions producing it.
2. Active listening—a behavior that makes voice feel worth it: A team can invite open and honest dialogue, but if people are met with distraction, impatience, defensiveness, or silence, they quickly learn that speaking up is costly and ineffective. Active listening signals, "Your voice matters and we are here to listen." It replaces assumptions with clarity, defensiveness with curiosity, and futility with evidence that speaking leads to learning or action.
3. The response after someone speaks is a defining moment: When a person raises a concern, asks a hard question, or shares an uncomfortable truth, the team's response teaches them whether to do that again. A weak response may sound polite on the surface but still communicate "This is not going anywhere." A stronger response protects the voice, seeks clarity, acknowledges the effort, and closes the loop. That is how teams make speaking up feel safer and more worthwhile over time.
4. Misalignment is often a listening problem disguised as an execution problem: Many breakdowns that show up later as rework, frustration, or missed expectations do not begin in execution. They begin much earlier, when people assume they understand, fail to verify meaning, or move forward on only partial alignment. The listening exercises in this chapter made that visible. Shallow listening leaves room for assumptions to fill the gaps. Active listening creates the pause needed to confirm meaning before misunderstanding becomes built into the work.

5. Small habits, big impact: Speaking up and active listening are built in small, repeatable moments: making space before responding, asking one more open question, paraphrasing what was heard, noticing what is not being said, inviting quieter voices in, and following up after the conversation ends. These habits may seem simple, but they shape whether the team becomes a place where people filter, delay, and protect themselves—or a place where truth travels earlier and coordination becomes stronger.

One Team is built on a foundation of speaking up and active listening. It means we do not just share what we think—we make room for what others are trying to say. It means we pay attention not only to the words but also to the meaning, context, and concerns behind them. It means we slow down just enough to clarify, to verify, and to respond with care. When listening is shallow, people start holding back. When listening is real, people speak sooner, ask questions earlier, and work through misunderstandings before they turn into rework or resentment.

In the next chapter, we explore what turns voice into reliability: the ability to make and keep promises. And if some of the ideas feel familiar, that is by design—reliable promises require the same speaking-up and listening moves you just practiced, now applied to coordination. You will see how commitments become stronger when teams can speak up about constraints, ask for clarity, and renegotiate expectations early—before trust takes a hit.

Chapter 6

Follow Through Together

Make Reliable Promises

Reliable promises are one of the clearest ways a team turns psychological safety into action people can depend on. Psychological safety makes it safer to tell the truth—about what you understand, what you do not, what you can do, and what you cannot. Reliable promises rely on that truth. They are one way teams protect each other's time, reduce late surprises, and coordinate interdependent work without burning people out. When promises are vague, rushed, or forced, teams compensate with guessing, overwork, reminders, and backup plans. But when promises are made deliberately—through clarification, negotiation, and clear conditions of satisfaction—"yes" becomes something other people can actually plan around. In One Team, "yes" is real, and "no" or "not yet" is safe to say.

The Many Ways a Promise Can Break Down

For a long time, I thought broken promises were mostly a character problem: someone was careless, disorganized, or simply not responsible enough. It took me years—and a handful of painful "yeses"—to understand something more complex: a promise can fall through for many reasons, and the breakdown often starts long before anyone misses a deadline.

Early in my career, I wanted to be the kind of teammate people could count on for everything. If someone needed something, I would find a way. That sounded like reliability, and sometimes it was. But underneath it, there was another driver: I struggled to say no—especially to people I looked up to. I began to notice that my "yes" came out automatically—sometimes before my brain had even finished processing what was being asked.

I remember one request vividly because it looked small on the surface. During one of my first internships, a senior leader asked if I could "pull together a quick summary" for an upcoming meeting. I said yes immediately—not because I had checked my workload or knew exactly what to do, but because how could I say no? I felt honored that he had even asked. So, I took the request and ran.

DOI: 10.1201/9781003734864-6

Only later—hours into the work—did I realize that I had never actually clarified what "quick summary" meant. Was it a one-page narrative or a full slide deck he could present to others? Did he want background context or just the key decisions made? Who was the audience? Was this meant to persuade, inform, or document? What level of detail would be "good"? I did not ask those questions. Instead, I guessed. And because I had guessed, I worked late into the night trying to cover every possible interpretation. I told myself I was being thorough. In reality, I was trading clarity for effort.

The next day I sent what I thought was a strong deliverable—clean, detailed, structured. The response came quickly: appreciative but followed by a comment that landed hard. "This is helpful, but it is not what I needed. I was looking for something much shorter just highlighting what we are deciding, what the team recommended, and next steps."

Nothing about his message was harsh. But it made the gap clear: I had delivered something on time, yet what I delivered was not what he needed.

My *aha moment* came later that week, as I reflected on what had happened. I realized the promise had not fallen through because I lacked commitment. It fell through because I had skipped the parts of promising that make a commitment reliable. I had said yes before confirming scope. Yes, before checking feasibility. Yes, before clarifying what I was actually supposed to deliver. And once I realized that, I saw how many ways a promise can fail even when everyone is well-intentioned: the request can be vague, "done" can mean different things to different people, assumptions can stay unspoken, the performer can be overloaded, timelines can be declared instead of negotiated. The miss is not always at the end. Often, it starts at the beginning.

At the time of the request, I did not see it that way. I saw only two options: accept the request or fail the relationship. Negotiation did not feel like a possibility. Counterproposals felt risky. Asking clarifying questions felt like revealing incompetence. So, I defaulted to "certainty"—even when I did not have it.

Later, when I started mentoring students, I began to notice a familiar pattern. That earlier lesson became even clearer. I would ask a student to complete something by a certain date, and they would say yes quickly—eager and confident. And then the same cycle would repeat: delays, rushed work, or a deliverable that technically arrived but did not meet expectations.

At first, I felt frustrated. I had deadlines too. I needed reliable handoffs. I started paying more attention to what was happening and what was missing. I could see myself in them: They were trying to be "good" students by saying yes—just like I used to. So, I changed what I rewarded. I stopped rewarding an immediate yes and started rewarding clarity before commitment. I stopped equating "no" with lack of commitment or lack of trying. I started treating it as useful information: a signal about capacity, clarity, or constraints. A "no" was not a rejection; it was an invitation to renegotiate the work so the commitment could actually hold. Students started saying, "I can do this part by Friday, but I will need another week to complete this other part," or "what are you expecting to see in this upcoming draft?" Those answers were a step in making the promise real.

This chapter is about promising differently: Moving from automatic yeses to reliable commitments—so "yes" becomes something other people can truly plan around, and "no" becomes safe to say. By the end of this chapter, you will be able to:

1. Explain why reliable promises are a core One Team behavior—and how psychological safety makes reliable promising possible.
2. Use the anatomy of a promise to diagnose breakdowns and improve follow-through.

3. Practice language that makes it safer to clarify, renegotiate, and say "no" when needed—without damaging trust.
4. Recognize when a "promise" is actually an order (non-negotiable compliance) and still apply the principles for making reliable promises.
5. Implement simple team routines that reduce overcommitment, surface constraints early, and turn missed commitments into prevention—not blame.

6.1 The Anatomy of Promises Grounded in Psychological Safety

People work better together when they can make reliable promises—commitments others can actually plan around. But, despite best efforts, we sometimes break our promises. Something you did not expect to happen gets in the way. Suppose Tom and Henry are planning to meet for lunch. They agree to meet at noon at Rosa's Taverna, but at 11:30, just as Tom is getting ready to leave his house, a water pipe underneath the kitchen sink breaks. He has to take care of this right away. He shuts off the water, then calls Henry to explain. Tom felt bad about breaking his promise to Henry, but Henry understood—some misses are truly unavoidable.

But other promises fail for avoidable reasons. Suppose Tom asks Henry if he can borrow his pipe wrench to fix the water leak. Henry agrees to loan Tom the wrench, but when Tom arrives to get it, Henry remembers that he loaned it to someone else. That breakdown was not caused by bad intent—it was caused by skipping a basic reliability check. Henry promised before verifying whether he was able to fulfill the promise (e.g., checking availability of resources). In both situations, the promise breaks—but for very different reasons. One is reality interrupting a feasible commitment. The other is a preventable miss created by skipping a step.

Reliable promises are created—not simply hoped for. A promise emerges from a conversation that follows a path. These conversations move through seven steps—from request to satisfaction—that turn "can you . . .?" into "you can count on me." Figure 42 illustrates Flores's *conversation for action* steps[1] and makes the psychological safety layer explicit—highlighting where people need to feel safe enough to ask, clarify, negotiate, and repair in ways that make reliability possible.

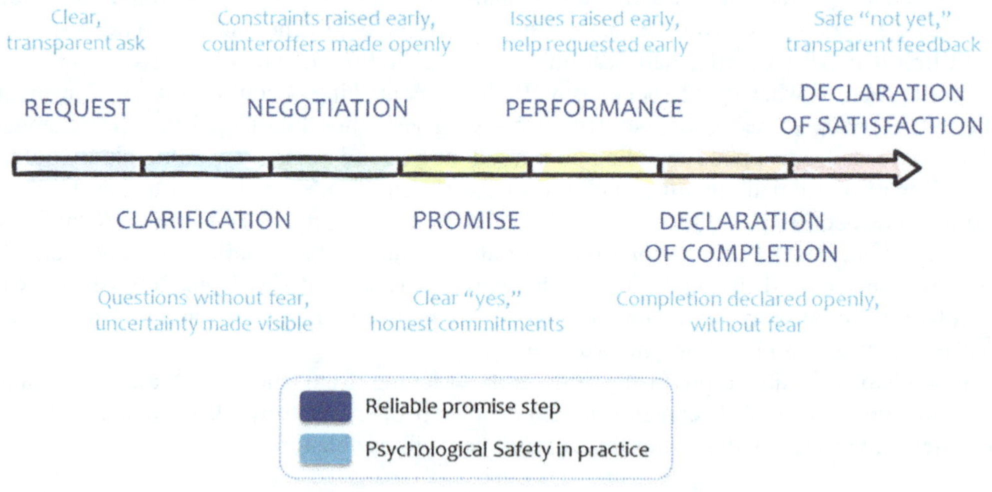

Figure 42 Psychological Safety in the Reliable Promises Cycle.

Source: Adapted from Flores (1982)

1. REQUEST: The requestor initiates the conversation by communicating their needs to the performer. A reliable request is a clear, transparent ask that makes it possible for the performer to answer honestly. If you are the one making a request, you can say, "I have a request. Would you . . .?" and then clearly state the expected outcome, timing, and what matters most. Psychological safety enables people to make a real request (not a vague hint) and to name what actually matters without fear of being seen as unreasonable or "too demanding."

Script (for Requestors)

"Here is the outcome I'm aiming for. Here is when I need it. Here is why the date matters. Can you take this on?"

2. CLARIFICATION: If you are the one receiving the request, first make sure you understand what is being asked. Here is a true story: Greg and his wife Dana drive up to their home. As they get out of the car, Dana says, "The grass is getting long." Greg's first reaction is to go get the lawn mower, but instead he says, "Are you asking me to cut the grass?" Dana says, "No, I just like the way it waves in the wind when it is longer." Dana was not making a request at all. If Greg had not asked for clarification, he would have done exactly what Dana did not want. Clarification means confirming the deliverable, the audience, the level of detail, and the conditions of satisfaction. If "done" is fuzzy, the promise is already unstable.

In a psychologically safe environment, the performer is able to ask "basic" questions, name uncertainty, and slow down long enough to verify meaning—without shame. The performer also evaluates whether they have the ability and resources to fulfill the request. If it is not safe to clarify, people guess. And guessed promises often become rework later.

Performer's Check (Conditions of Satisfaction)

Before making a commitment, the performer should make sure the request is clear and that they understand what success requires.

- What does "done" look like?
- When is it due?
- Who is the audience/user?
- What format and level of detail are expected?
- Are there specific quality standards or examples I should follow?
- What is in/out of scope?
- What do I need before I can start (inputs/decisions/access)?

3. NEGOTIATION: Both parties engage in a negotiation to reach a mutual agreement on the promise. Negotiation is not resistance—it is how teams create feasible commitments. This may involve discussing timelines, resources, limitations, and tradeoffs. If capacity is not discussed in this step, it will be discovered later—through delays, rework, and burnout. Psychological safety is what makes it possible to say, "I cannot do that as asked," to propose a

counteroffer, to name constraints early, and to say no without fear of punishment or damaged relationships.

Script (Normalizing Negotiation)

"I cannot commit to that as stated. Here is what I can commit to, given my current constraints."

Examples

"I can own Steps 1–3 if someone else owns Steps 4–5."
"If you need ___ by Friday, I will need ___ by Wednesday."

4. PROMISE[2]: If you can reach an agreement in the negotiation step, then a promise is made and accepted. This commitment signifies the performer's dedication to following through on their word. Psychological safety supports a clean "yes" here: people can commit without overpromising, and they can be honest about what they are (and are not) taking ownership of. A reliable promise includes the "what," the "when," and any key conditions the team agreed to.

Script (Promising Language)

"Yes—I commit to [the deliverable] by [this date/time], with [these conditions]."

5. PERFORMANCE: The promise is carried out. The performer takes action to fulfill the promise according to the agreed-upon terms. Psychological safety matters during performance because people must feel safe to raise issues early—request help, flag emerging risks, or renegotiate when conditions change—instead of hiding problems until it is too late. This is where reliability is either protected—or quietly lost. Early issue-raising is not a weakness; it is a reliability move. It is also a respect move: it protects everyone downstream from planning on something that is already slipping.

6. DECLARATION OF COMPLETION: "I have kept my promise." After delivering the promised outcome, the performer declares the completion of their commitment. This step serves as a formal acknowledgment that the promise has been fulfilled. Psychological safety supports transparency here: people can clearly declare completion and name any remaining gaps without fear that honesty will be used against them. This prevents "silent handoffs" where others assume that the work is done—or discover late that it is not.

Note on Closing the Loop

Completion is not just "sent." Completion is "received and acknowledged." Reliability also means closing the loop.

7. DECLARATION OF SATISFACTION: "Thank you" or "No, you did not do X and Y as we agreed. Let's see what happened." If the requestor is satisfied with the performance, they say "Thank you," otherwise, they explain their dissatisfaction. Then the requestor and performer together try to understand what caused the failure and how to prevent it in the future. Psychological safety allows for a conversation where "not yet" is safe to say, and feedback can be discussed openly.

When a commitment is missed, treat it as data: clarify what was misunderstood, adjust conditions of satisfaction, renegotiate what is feasible, and recommit—so the breakdown becomes a source of learning rather than resentment.

Note to Focus on Prevention

After a missed commitment, use this question to help the team identify where the breakdown occurred and what to do differently next time:

Where in the reliable promises cycle did the breakdown occur—and what will we do differently next time?

Table 3 builds on the seven steps above by showing, in more detail, how psychological safety supports reliable promises at each step. It translates psychological safety into behaviors that support reliability: stating requests clearly, asking clarifying questions without fear, naming constraints early, treating negotiation as accountability (not pushback), making a clean promise that matches reality, surfacing issues early during performance, declaring completion clearly, and confirming satisfaction without blame.

Before making a promise, ask: "What questions am I not asking because I do not want to look incompetent?" "What constraint am I hesitating to name?" "What counteroffer would make this feasible?" During performance, pause to consider: "Am I staying silent about a risk because it feels socially unsafe to raise?" At closure, make the final two moves explicit: declaring completion clearly and confirming satisfaction directly. When teams practice the behaviors in Table 3, reliability improves because the truth shows up earlier—when it is early enough to respond and adjust.

Teams that are better at promising spend less energy guessing and more energy delivering—because "yes" becomes something you can truly plan around. Promises become the building blocks of coordination. When we understand what a promise actually represents—who plans around it, what it protects, and what it costs when it fails—we start treating it as a shared way

Table 3 Psychological Safety as an Enabler of Reliable Promises

Step	*Psychological Safety Enables*
Request: Requestor states what they need	• Making clear requests (not hints, not a vague "can you handle this?"). • Being transparent about what matters: outcome, timing, quality. • Inviting questions up front.
Clarification: Performer checks understanding	• Asking "basic" questions without worrying they will look incompetent. • Naming uncertainty early ("I'm not sure what you mean by 'ready' . . ."). • Slowing down to verify meaning instead of rushing to look capable. • Surfacing dependencies early ("I cannot start until . . ."). • Restating what was understood and checking that both people mean the same thing.
Negotiation: Parties shape a feasible commitment	• Making counteroffers without being labeled "not a team player." • Naming capacity and priorities (workload, sequencing, resourcing). • Surfacing constraints early (access, approvals, information, equipment, safety, rework risk). • Saying "no," "not yet," or "not like that" without fear of punishment. • Receiving a counteroffer or "no" as useful information rather than a lack of commitment.
Promise: A clear commitment is made and accepted	• Giving an honest "yes," not one given to gain or preserve approval. • Committing without overpromising (what is / is not included). • Asking for what is needed to keep the promise ("Yes, if I have___ by ___").
Performance: Work is executed; conditions might change	• Raising risks early instead of hiding them until failure becomes inevitable. • Asking for help without embarrassment or fear of judgment. • Renegotiating when reality changes ("Here is what changed; here is my proposal").
Declaration of completion: Performer states completion	• Clearly declaring completion and making the handoff explicit so the requestor knows the work is ready for review. • Being transparent about any remaining gaps or constraints.
Declaration of satisfaction: Requestor confirms status	• Saying "thank you" or "not yet/missed X" without blame or humiliation. • Giving feedback that is specific and actionable. • Receiving feedback without defensiveness and treating it as input. • Working together to repair a missed commitment and determine what happens next.

of working. That deeper meaning of a promise—and why it matters so much for working as a team—is what we unpack next.

6.2 The Meaning of a Promise

The significance of a promise is easy to underestimate because it often sounds ordinary: "I will have it by Friday." "I will take care of it." "We will be ready." But underneath those phrases sits something bigger: a promise is a basic unit of coordination that One Team relies on to get the work done. You can feel it anytime your day depends on someone else's "I've got it."

We see this in everyday life. When we drive, we operate on a web of implicit promises: I will stop at red lights, signal my turns, and stay in my lane. When most people keep these promises, traffic flows and accidents are rare. When enough people ignore them, chaos and harm follow. On projects, we live inside a similar web of promises—only now the stakes include safety, quality, cost, and relationships. When promises hold, work can flow. When they do not, teams start building "just in case" buffers, backup plans, and workarounds that quietly drain trust and time. That is how unreliable promising creates waste: the team spends more energy protecting itself than delivering value.

6.2.1 Plans That Become Reality

A promise tells the next person: you can plan on this—not hope for it. Schedules are full of assumptions: "inspections done by Tuesday," "drawings updated before the next pour." Often, these are built on educated guesses but do not mean much until someone commits to carry out the tasks. Reliable promises give teams a better way to coordinate and get work done together:

- Sets clear expectations: It answers "what," "by when," and "what good looks like," so people downstream can plan their work.
- Signals acceptance of accountability: It tells others, "You can build your plan on this," which is very different from "we will try."
- Builds trust: Reliability is built through a pattern of commitments that people can depend on.

You can feel the impact of promises on something as simple as material delivery. Imagine a foreman is told, "Rebar will be on site Friday morning." On that promise, the team schedules the crew, crane time, and a concrete pour. If the delivery shows up as promised, the day unfolds as planned. If it does not, the consequences ripple: idle crews, costly rescheduling, stress, and frustration. And even when the team "recovers," the hidden bill remains: lost flow, rushed decisions, and the quiet lesson people learn—"do not trust."

Some planning breakdowns begin when:

- Assumptions get mistaken for promises ("It should be ready by then." "They will probably finish").
- Promises are made without enough definition to be usable ("We will clean it up." "We will send the update").

One way to prevent these is to make "plan-ready" the standard: Who owns it? What exactly will be true when it is done? By when? And what does it depend on? If any one of those is unclear, the team is not holding a promise yet—they are holding hope.

After enough misses, people stop treating promises as reliable inputs and start checking and protecting against uncertainty: "Let's wait and see," "I will send someone to verify," "I will line up a backup crew just in case." This is where "buffers" begin to grow. That response is rational—but expensive. The team pays in time, focus, and morale.

Promising better is about making commitments safe, clear, and real—so people can coordinate with confidence and adjust together when reality changes. Reliable promises protect flow and people: fewer chases, fewer surprises, and less burnout.

Facilitator Note (Mapping Promises)

Invite the team to look at one upcoming week of work and circle every place where a promise is implied. Ask:

- Who owns this?
- Have they explicitly accepted the commitment?
- What must be true for them to keep it?
- What will we do if a key condition changes?

Reviewing the upcoming work this way often reveals where teams are planning around assumptions rather than actual commitments.

6.2.2 *Non-Negotiables*

Reliable promises depend on real choice. But work is not that simple. Some situations are, by design, non-negotiable. If you see a coworker stepping backward toward a moving piece of equipment, you do not open a dialogue; you shout, "Stop!" If a fire alarm goes off in a packed building, there is no time for a planning session; people must follow the evacuation plan right away. On construction sites, certain rules—lockout/tagout, fall protection, confined space procedures—are not optional. In such moments, saying "no" is not an option. However, being clear about what you are being directed to do is still absolutely necessary. They exist precisely because someone got hurt (or worse) when the rules were not followed.

In these cases, the organization is not asking for a promise in the sense of "Would you be willing to . . .?" It is issuing a directive: "You must." And that is appropriate. Safety and emergency responses rely on immediate action, not negotiation. In that moment, compliance is the commitment.

But even in non-negotiable situations, the principles of reliable promising still apply—just at different moments in time. Two patterns stand out:

- Planning with voices from the field: Before we ever get to the moment of "Do this now," there is usually time to plan how work will be done. Captain Wilcox's story[3] illustrates this. Leading a U.S. Navy construction battalion in Vietnam, he would call meetings with officers and sergeants to plan tasks like building a road through the jungle. At the start of the meeting, he asked everyone to place their insignia in a bowl on the table—signaling that, in that room, rank was set aside so people could speak freely. In that space, people could question assumptions, raise risks, and propose better methods. Later, in the field, orders had to be followed quickly. But those orders were grounded in plans shaped by the people who understood the work.
- Encouraging initiative within clear boundaries: On a nuclear submarine, one captain adopted a practice where officers would say, "Captain, I intend to . . .," describing the action they were about to take.[4] If the captain did not intervene, they proceeded. This did

not remove his authority; it created a structure where others could act with responsibility and transparency inside agreed limits.

In both examples, formal authority remains intact—but it is used in a way that invites participation, surfaces assumptions, and clarifies expectations before the moment of command. That is where the spirit of reliable promising shows up: in the preparation, in the shared understanding of what "we will do," and in the debriefs afterward when things go right or wrong. This is also where psychological safety shows up—even in non-negotiables—because the team needs a space where someone can say, "This plan will not work," before the consequences become more difficult to manage.

A directive can be non-negotiable and still be well-designed. The difference is whether the planning conversation happened early enough for the team's knowledge to shape a safer, more reliable way of carrying out the work.

Outside of true emergencies, most work benefits from conversation. A supervisor still has authority, but how they use it matters. "Do this by Friday, no questions," sends a different signal than, "Here is what we need, here is why Friday matters—tell me what you need to make that possible." If people do not feel safe to question, clarify, or say, "I cannot do that safely/by then," the organization loses two things at once: reliable promises and critical information from the people doing the work. Plans might look good on paper but still fail in practice.

One practical way to keep this from staying abstract is to name it as a team norm: In emergencies, we act. Outside emergencies, we clarify and negotiate early—so we do not discover "this will not work" in the field or by the deadline.

Now that we have explored the implications of a promise, the next question becomes practical: how do we manage promises in the reality of work?

6.3 Managing Promises Together

On real projects, promises rarely stay in a neat, linear sequence. They are made in hallways, during handoffs, inside huddles, in texts, and in quick "can you . . .?" moments when pressure is high. This means reliability cannot depend on one person's memory or individual effort. It has to be managed as a shared practice—visible enough that the team can coordinate around it, and flexible enough that it can be updated when reality changes.

A clear promise tells others, "You can plan with me." A renegotiated promise tells them, "You will not be surprised by me." And a repaired promise tells them, "We can tell the truth here, learn, and move forward together."

So, the question becomes: how can promises be managed as One Team—early—before they turn into rework, reminders, or resentment? One place to start is by distinguishing a good intention from a reliable commitment.

6.3.1 *Promises You Can Plan Around*

Two promises can sound equally committed and still function very differently once work starts. Figure 43 shows this contrast.

In the first promise—"Humberto promised he would clean the work area"—the intent may be genuine, but the commitment is underspecified. The team is left to guess: Which area? Clean to what standard? By when? Ready for what next step? What constraints apply? When conditions of satisfaction are missing, different mental models fill the gap—and the promise becomes unstable even if the performer works hard.

Humberto promised he would clean the work area

Humberto promised he would clean the 4th floor-zone 1 by noon 23/08/14 with ABC equipment so it is ready for inspection

Figure 43 Example of Promising Better.

In the second promise, the commitment becomes operational: the scope is specific (Floor 4-Zone 1), the time is explicit (by noon, 23/08/14), a required resource or constraint is named (ABC equipment needs to be available), and the purpose is clear (ready for inspection). This is a promise that others can actually plan around—because it reduces guessing and allows downstream work to coordinate with confidence.

Facilitator Note

Use the example in Figure 43—or one relevant to the team's own work—to explore what makes a promise reliable enough to plan around. Ask the group:

- "Which promise would you rather build your plan around—and why?"
- "What questions would you need answered to make the first promise better?"

Teams rarely lose reliability because people do not care. They lose reliability because commitments are made faster than understanding. When "done" stays implicit in someone's head, the promise turns into a guess: the performer guesses what success looks like, the requestor guesses what they will receive, and everyone downstream guesses how to coordinate.

To shift that risk earlier, teams can begin by adding a few practical moves to the conversations teams already have—handoffs, huddles, and coordination moments—so promises become clearer, more feasible, and easier to update when conditions change. The following practice conversations provide a place to start.

Practice Conversation: Conditions of Satisfaction

Use this for any task or cross-role handoff where "done" could be interpreted in multiple ways.

A One-Line Template

Deliverable + scope + conditions of satisfaction + deadline + constraints.

"I will deliver [what/scope] by [when], meeting [conditions of satisfaction], assuming [constraints free]."

Use prompts such as:

- What would make you say "thanks—this is exactly what we needed"?
- What would make you say, "not yet"?
- What has to be true before the work can start? (access, equipment, approvals, prerequisite work).

Implementation Tip

Ask for one example of "good" (a photo, a past deliverable, a mockup, a marked-up sketch) to better understand expectations. Examples anchor the quality benchmark more clearly than words alone.

Practice Conversation: The "No Surprises" Midpoint Signal

Use this when work is complex, takes a long time to complete, or has significant downstream impact—and getting too far before discovering misalignment would be costly.

Performer Script

"Here is a preview. Am I on track with what you need?"

Implementation Tip

Schedule the midpoint check when the commitment is made. Choose a point early enough that there is still room to adjust if expectations, conditions, or priorities have changed. The goal is to confirm that the work is still on track before too much progress is made in the wrong direction.

Practice It

- Ask each person to choose one upcoming deliverable that would benefit from a midpoint check.
- Have them identify when the right point to check in would be and what they would share to make progress visible.
- Then ask them to draft a short message they could use, such as: "Here is where I am so far. Before I continue, I want to make sure I'm still on track with what you need."
- Pair up and review the messages together: Is it clear what is being shared? Is it clear what feedback is needed before moving forward?

These practical conversations help teams make promises clearer and stronger, but they only work when people feel safe enough to use them honestly. This matters most when the honest answer is, "I cannot meet that timeline," "I need help," or "this will not work as planned." If those truths feel risky to say, clarity will still break down under pressure. Reliable promises therefore depend on both sound coordination practices and an environment where people can clarify, renegotiate, and repair commitments openly as work unfolds.

6.3.2 Living Agreements

Psychological safety is what allows teams to treat promises as living agreements instead of rigid ultimatums. In a psychologically safe team, a promise is not just "kept or missed," it is actively managed as conditions change. People can say, "I'm at risk of missing this; here is why, and here is my proposal," without fear of humiliation or punishment. They can admit misunderstanding early. They can ask for help without shame. And they can repair a miss without turning it into a personal attack.

A simple rule sits at the heart of this: *If it is not safe to say "no," "not yet," or "yes, if. . ." then the team does not actually have promises—it has compliance and hidden risk.* When saying "no" or naming a constraint is punished, people may say "yes" even when the commitment is unrealistic. Reliability cannot be built on that kind of fear.

Some practices that support this kind of reliability include:

Boundaries and respect: In a psychologically safe environment, people can name their limits without being labeled difficult or disloyal. A crew member can say, "I cannot do that safely without a lift," and the leader should treat that as valuable information, not insubordination. Respecting a "no" (or a conditional "yes, if . . .") prevents burnout, shortcuts, and unsafe workarounds.

Transparent capacity and priorities: Reliable promises require a realistic view of the workload. When people can openly say, "Here is what I'm already committed to," the team can negotiate priorities instead of silently overloading. Declining a request—or proposing a different timeline—can be understood as protecting the reliability of the commitment rather than as a lack of commitment.

Requests framed as such: Many tasks can be approached as requests rather than orders, for example, asking "Can you take this on?" instead of "You must." When people feel they have a voice in what they commit to, their "yes" carries more weight. They are more likely to speak up early if something changes, because they have been treated as partners, not just resources.

Supportive leadership: Leaders set the tone. When they react defensively to concerns, people go quiet. When they respond with curiosity—"Tell me more about why this does not feel safe/realistic"—they create room for voice, making more informed decisions. Leaders who invite dissenting views, listen to constraints, and back people up when they refuse unsafe work are not just being kind; they are building reliability into the system.

Consider a familiar scenario on a project: a supervisor, under pressure, tells a worker to remove a guardrail "just for a bit" to speed up an activity. A worker who feels unsafe speaking up might comply, hoping nothing bad happens. A worker in a psychologically safe environment can say, "I cannot do that—it violates our safety policies. We need another way." In the second case, the organization honors its own principles, and the commitment shifts from "we will get it done at any cost" to "let's find a way to get it done without putting someone at risk." That is reliability in a healthy team: the team still commits—but within the boundaries that protect people.

6.3.3 Broken Promises

When promises are repeatedly broken, a quieter pattern emerges: people stop trusting what they hear. They nod in meetings but make backup plans "just in case." They build extra buffers into dates, double-book resources, or avoid surfacing constraints because they do not believe commitments will hold. Over time, this erosion of trust shows up as:

- Hesitation to rely on others ("I will just do it myself").
- Withholding information ("If I do not trust your date, why should I share mine?").
- More conflict and blame when things slip ("You said you would have it done").
- Silence around problems ("What is the point of speaking up? It will not change anything").

Figure 44 captures what often sits underneath a visible miss: the performer carries hidden costs like guilt, loss of self-trust, a damaged reputation, and strained relationships—while the requestor carries disappointment, resentment, and an erosion of trust that weakens collaboration.

Figure 45 highlights how repeated misses do not just create isolated frustration—they create a downward drift in team behavior. When reliability drops, people instinctively protect themselves: they rely less, share less early, and wait to see what happens before committing to their own next steps. Those responses become patterns that make getting work done together more difficult.

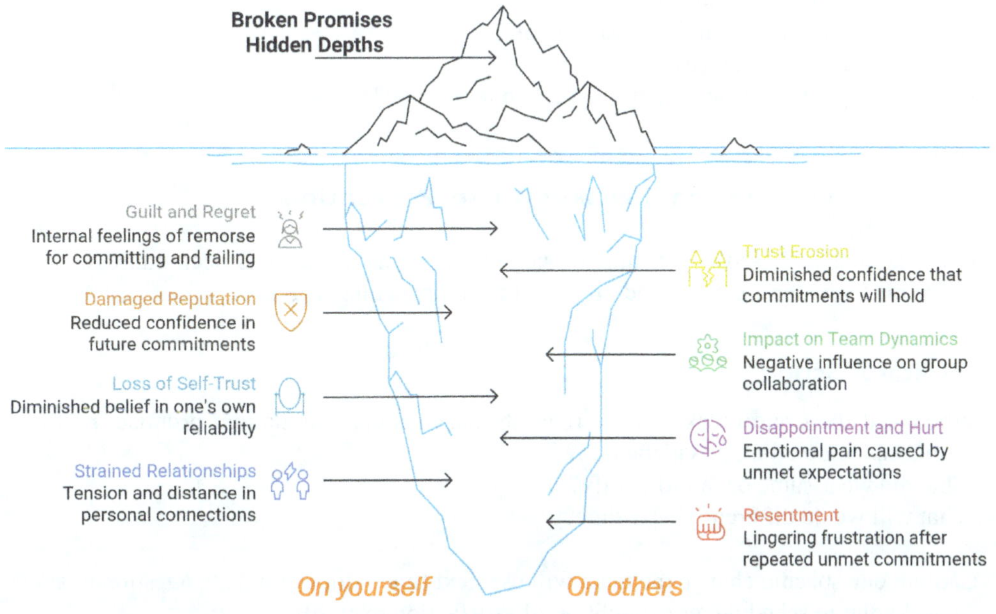

Figure 44 What Breaks When Promises Break.

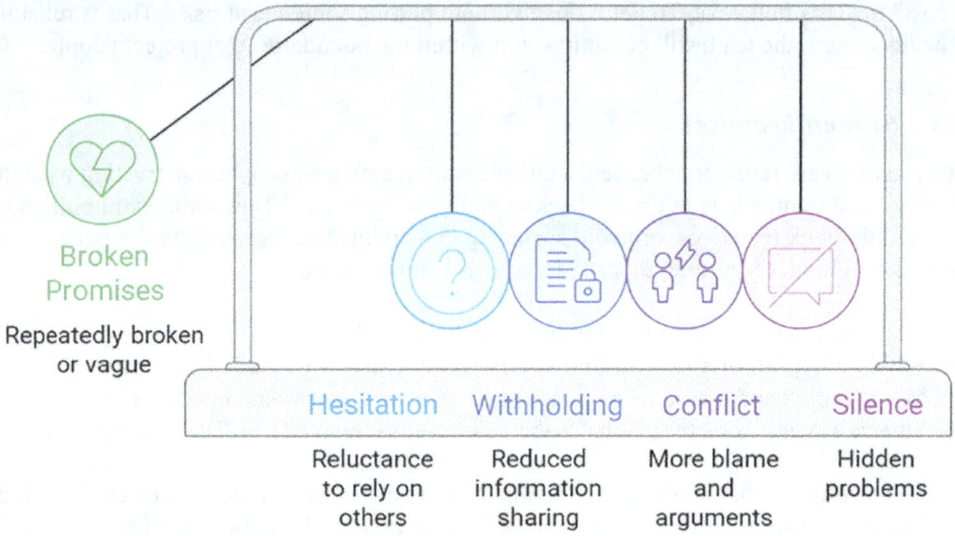

Figure 45 From Broken Promises to Silence.

So, what do we do when a promise breaks? Instead of defaulting to blame, look for where the breakdown occurred:

- Was the request unclear?
- Were conditions of satisfaction missing or assumed?
- Was capacity overestimated?
- Were constraints not surfaced early enough?
- Was negotiation avoided?
- Was completion declared and satisfaction confirmed?

Practice Conversation: Breakdown-to-Prevention

Use this after a missed commitment, once the immediate issue has been addressed, to understand what broke down and prevent it from happening again.

Facilitator Script

Where did the cycle break—at the request, clarification, negotiation, promise, performance, completion, or satisfaction?
What did we assume or fail to clarify?
What will we do differently next time?

Capture one specific change the team will use next time—for example, a question to ask, a checkpoint to schedule, or a condition of satisfaction to clarify.

This shifts the conversation from "Who dropped the ball?" to "Which part of our promising system needs strengthening?" That is how teams improve reliability not at the expense of people. Once we can diagnose where promises break, the next step is prevention—building the habit of examining what broke down and what needs to change next time.

The next section translates the promise cycle into daily moves—what to say when you are making the request, what to ask before you commit, what to do when conditions change, and how to close the loop so "done" becomes real and trust continues to build.

6.4 Promising Better in Action

Reliable promises are where teamwork becomes real. On real projects, one person's commitment becomes another person's input to plan their work. Plans only hold when commitments hold—and commitments only hold when people can be honest about what is understood, what is missing, what is feasible, and what support is required.

Why Does This Matter Now?

Often, the real cost of unreliable promises is not one missed date—it is the defensive behaviors that follow: double-checking everything, buffering schedules, staying silent, or hiding risks until there is no room left to adjust. Promising better protects trust and builds a culture where "yes" actually means yes, and "no" or "not yet" are safe.

What Does It Look Like in Daily Team Interactions?

It shows up in the small moments teams barely label as "promising": a quick ask in a hallway, a handoff at the end of a meeting, a text that says, "I will send it later," or a superintendent asking, "Can you make this ready?" These moments shape whether work becomes something others can truly plan around or something they quietly hedge against. Reliable promising is built through the small actions that help teams make commitments clearer and easier to manage when conditions change:

Make Requests That Can Be Promised

- State the request clearly: what you need, by when, and the conditions of satisfaction.
- Invite clarification upfront: "What do you need to know before you can commit?"
- Share the reason behind the request when it helps the performer assess timing, trade-offs, and what matters most: "I need it by Thursday because it unlocks ___."
- Respect the right to say "no," "not yet," or make a counteroffer.

Clarify Before Commit

- Confirm a shared understanding of success: "So you want ___ by ___, and it needs to include ___."
- Ask for what is missing or in the way: examples, constraints, access, approvals.
- Do not accept a request you do not fully understand. Getting clarity is not a delay; it helps prevent issues downstream.

Check Capacity Before Saying Yes

- Make your capacity visible: "Here is what I'm already committed to this week."
- Confirm feasibility before agreeing: "Given my current load, I can commit to ___, but not ___."
- Use conditional commitments openly: "Yes, if I have X by Wednesday."

Normalize Negotiation

- If the timeline is not feasible, offer an alternative: "I can deliver Y by Friday and Z by Tuesday—would that work?"
- If priorities conflict, surface the tradeoff: "If I take this on, it will delay ___. Which should we prioritize?"
- Treat negotiation as accountability, not pushback: A negotiated promise is more reliable than an optimistic "yes."
- If a promise is at risk, communicate early with a revised plan: "Here is what changed; here is what we can do").

Close the Loop—Especially When Something Slips

- Declare completion: "I have delivered ___." Then ask the requestor to confirm satisfaction: "Does this meet what you needed?" Anything to adjust?"
- When a promise breaks, focus on learning and prevention: "Where did the promise cycle break down, and what will we do differently next time?"

Remember, a reliable promise is not "I will try." It is "Here is what I commit to, here is what it depends on, and here is how we will manage it if conditions change."

What Does It Look Like at the Organizational Level?

Reliable promises take root when they are not dependent on a few high-performing individuals but built into how the organization coordinates. Organizations strengthen reliability when they:

- Make capacity visible (work-in-progress limits, clear priorities, and realistic deadlines).
- Normalize negotiation (tradeoff conversations, escalation paths, and room to propose alternatives).
- Create follow-through systems (simple trackers for handoffs, owners, and due dates).
- Turn missed commitments into prevention (brief retrospectives that lead to changes, not blame).
- Reinforce behaviors that support reliability (renegotiating early, clarifying "done," declaring completion, confirming satisfaction).

Start Small and Start Now

Start with the commitments already in front of you. Take a moment to reflect:

- Are there commitments you are making now that need to be renegotiated, clarified, or recommitted to?
- What is one routine you can adopt this week to make your commitments more reliable?

Practices for Reliable Promises

The clarity check: Before you say yes, ask one question that clarifies the definition of "done."
The capacity pause: Before you commit, state your current load and confirm feasibility.
The renegotiate early rule: If a promise is at risk, communicate as soon as possible and propose a revised plan.
The close-the-loop habit: When you complete the work, confirm satisfaction instead of assuming it.

6.5 Highlights

Reliable promises are one of the clearest ways a team turns good intentions into coordinated action. They are not just about keeping your word in a personal sense; they are about making your word usable to others. In team settings, a promise is never isolated. It becomes part of how other people plan, sequence work, manage risk, and decide whether they can move forward with confidence.

Key ideas explored:

1. Promises are coordination: Every "yes" becomes someone else's input. When promises are reliable, teams coordinate with confidence, reduce guessing, and manage interdependent work together.
2. Reliability is built before the work begins. Many promises are already at risk long before the deadline—when requests are vague, conditions of satisfaction are assumed, constraints remain unspoken, or people say yes before they fully understand what is being asked. The promise cycle helps teams see where reliability is strengthened—or lost—from the initial request through delivery.
3. Psychological safety supports reliability: Saying "yes" means more when "no" is a real option. People can make reliable promises when they feel safe to ask questions, surface constraints, request help, and say "no" (or "not yet") without punishment or shame.
4. Leaders shape the conditions for reliable promising: Leaders do more than assign work—they influence whether people feel safe enough to clarify, negotiate, raise risks early, and renegotiate when reality changes. When leaders reward fast agreement, teams learn to say yes too quickly. When leaders invite questions, surface tradeoffs, and respond well to early warning signs, they help create the conditions for more reliable commitments.
5. Not all commitments are negotiable, but they still require clarity and preparation: In emergencies and safety-critical situations, immediate compliance may be necessary. But even then, reliability still depends on what happens before and after the moment of command (planning the work well, inviting input early, making expectations clear, and learning from what happened afterward).
6. Breakdowns are learning opportunities: When a promise breaks, the most useful question is not "Who failed?" but "Where did the promise become unreliable?" That shift helps teams move from blame to diagnosis, and from frustration to prevention.

One Team is built on promises people can rely on. It means we do not just say yes quickly—we make sure yes is real. It means we do not hide confusion, constraints, or risk—we bring them forward while there is still time to respond. It means we do not treat renegotiation as failure—we treat it as part of protecting each other's work. Because when promises are rushed or forced, people start protecting themselves. When promises are made clearly and honestly, people can plan, adjust, and follow through together.

In the next chapter, we shift from these core behaviors to collective momentum: how teams reflect, learn, and evolve together—so reliability and trust do not depend on a few people but on the team's shared routines that keep improving and growing as One.

Notes

1 Flores's (1982) dissertation, *Management and Communication in the Office of the Future*, proposes a structure for how commitments work. This book, *Building One Team*, adds the behavioral conditions that make that structure possible on real teams (e.g., psychological safety to ask clarifying questions, safety to negotiate and offer counterproposals, and safety to say "no" when capacity is not there).

2 Macomber and Howell (2003) said that a "promise can be considered reliable when the person making it can say,

'I am competent to perform or I have access to competence'
'I estimate it will take so much time'
'I have the capacity and I will allocate it'
'I am not having a private unspoken conversation in conflict with the promise'
'I will be responsible (willing to clean up any mess that ensues).'"

3 This story was originally shared by Gregory (Greg) Howell, Lt. Commander in the U.S. Navy, co-founder of the Lean Construction Institute, and co-creator of the Last Planner® System. Greg often used this example to illustrate how setting aside rank during planning creates conditions for candor, shared ownership, and better decision-making before execution begins. The version included here reflects that teaching tradition.

4 In the book, *Turn the Ship Around!: A True Story of Turning Followers into Leaders*, Captain Marquet describes using an "I intend to . . ." practice on the USS Santa Fe to shift decision-making away from pure permission-seeking and toward responsible action within clear boundaries.

Chapter 7

Grow as One

From Reflection to Transformation

> You can't announce One Team into existence. You build it—together—through repeatable routines that make healthy ways of working possible, especially in the moments that matter most.
>
> (Sulyn Gomez)

This book is not asking teams to "try harder." Most teams already are. Their struggle is rarely a lack of effort; more often, it is not having a practical way to turn insights into action. I still remember the moment when a team looked at me after an introduction to psychological safety and said, "This all makes sense . . . but what do we actually do tomorrow?" That question stayed with me. It revealed something important: awareness is necessary, but awareness alone does not change a team. The gap between understanding and practice is where many well-intentioned efforts stall. Teams become healthier when they turn awareness and reflection into repeatable action—when voice leads to commitments, commitments lead to follow-through, and follow-through leads to a better way of working together. That is where transformation begins.

By transformation, we mean building a team rhythm for seeing what is real, choosing what matters most, acting on it together, and staying with those actions long enough for new habits to take hold. It is the disciplined practice of turning the behaviors in this book into a shared way of working—so that truth can surface, people can stay whole, commitments can hold, and learning can continue under pressure. As you embark on this journey of transformation, remember: Start small. Make it visible. Revisit it. Be consistent. And keep one north star in view:

A healthy team is one where people excel at work and stay whole while doing it.

When we say, "healthy teams," we do not mean teams without tensions, disagreement, or breakdowns. We mean teams that have a way of working through those realities together: teams that can tell the truth without turning honesty into a threat, learn while the work is still moving, make and keep commitments without damaging relationships, and respond to pressure without defaulting to fear, blame, or silence. In healthy teams, candor and care coexist, commitments do not come at the expense of relationships, and performance does not come at the expense of people.

DOI: 10.1201/9781003734864-7

By this point, we have explored the core behavioral elements for building One Team (Figure 46):

- Psychological safety makes it safer for people to speak up without having to armor up first.
- Respect shows people that they matter—not only for the work they do, but for who they are. It is reflected in how we plan with others, respond to concerns, develop capabilities, recognize contributions, and protect dignity and wellbeing.
- Active learning helps teams turn questions, mistakes, experiments, and successes into shared insight and better ways of working.
- Active caring helps ensure that concern for others is not left as a feeling but becomes visible through actions that protect people, work, and relationships.
- Speaking up and active listening help teams surface what is real and stay in dialogue long enough to understand and act on it.
- Reliable promises turn that dialogue into commitments and follow-through that others can plan around.

The work ahead is to help teams practice these behaviors consistently enough for them to become a shared way of working, learning, and growing as One.

This chapter focuses on how teams turn these behaviors into repeatable practice: how they reflect on where they are, decide what to work on, take action together, and sustain progress when change feels awkward, uneven, or slow. The goal is to build a rhythm teams can return to so that One Team becomes visible in how they work together every day.

Figure 46 Core Elements for Building One Team.

7.1 From Intention to Readiness

Most teams already care deeply about doing better, but as we saw in earlier chapters, care alone does not create change. Readiness is the bridge between "we care" and "we are ready to act on that care." Without readiness, even well-meaning discussions can collapse into defensiveness, vague agreement, politeness, blame, or a flood of ideas that never become action.

We have seen this repeatedly in practice: *people only give the team what the environment can hold.* When reflection feels risky, you get silence, politeness, and safe generalities—enough to look cooperative, but not enough to improve. When reflection feels safe, people offer what the team actually needs: specific examples, early warnings, and feedback the team can use. The work of readiness, then, is to create conditions where people can speak honestly and their input can be used constructively. A team that is ready has enough trust, clarity, and structure to do that without the conversation turning into blame or defensiveness.

If these conversations feel awkward at the beginning, it may be because you are practicing something we rarely practice on purpose: talking about *how* we work together—especially while we are still executing the work. Several things make these conversations hard:

- People interpret "team improvement" as a personal critique.
- Past attempts may have failed, making skepticism understandable.
- Differences in role, status, and authority can shape how risky it feels to speak up.
- Time pressure pushes teams to default to execution over planning and reflection.
- Teams often lack a shared language for behaviors (respect, listening, promises) until they intentionally develop one.
- In many work cultures, "being tough" gets rewarded more than "being clear"—even though clarity is what prevents the chaos that harms both results and wellbeing.

Readiness has two foundations. One is internal: the willingness of each team member to reflect honestly, stay open, and participate with humility. The other is shared: the team creates enough structure and supportive conditions so that people believe reflection will be useful—not weaponized, ignored, or reduced to talk without follow-through. Both foundations matter. A team can have a process on paper but still go nowhere if individuals are not willing to engage sincerely. And a team can have well-intentioned individuals and still struggle if the collective environment makes honesty too costly.

Self-awareness matters because our words, actions, and silences shape what other people believe is safe. Ask yourself: "How did I contribute to the environment this week? Where did I make it easier—or harder—for someone else to speak? What is one behavior I will practice differently next time?" This helps the team hold both questions at once: "What is happening around me?" and "What can I do differently?"

Structure matters just as much. It means creating a clear purpose ("why we are here"), simple conversation norms ("how we talk here"), and a practical output ("what we will try next"). It also means deciding where commitments will live (a board, log, or channel), who owns them, and when they will be reviewed again. Without structure, people may speak up once and then learn it was not worth it. With structure, the team starts building credibility: "We surfaced it, we decided, we acted, we revisited." If the first few honest inputs are met with blame, defensiveness, or silence, people learn a fast lesson: do not risk it. But if the team responds with curiosity, dignity, and follow-through, people learn the opposite: it is safe enough to tell the truth here—and it leads somewhere.

Before asking a team to reflect on how it is working together, pause and ask: Are we ready to hear what we are about to uncover? Are we prepared to protect candor? Are we prepared to turn input into visible action?

Use Table 4 as a readiness check before you run a reflection-to-action conversation. This table translates "readiness" into practical setup moves—what to watch for, what to say, and what to

Table 4 Readiness for Reflection-to-Action

Readiness Focus	*Why It Matters*	*Practical Moves*
Set the mindset: "We can tell the truth and still belong"	People are more willing to engage when they understand that this is a learning conversation.	• Set a clear purpose: "We are here to understand how we are working together and identify what we can improve." • Frame honesty as a contribution to the team: "Say what you see, even when it is difficult to raise. We will focus on understanding it and deciding what we can do about it."
Encourage individual reflection before group candor	Individual reflection helps people consider what they are experiencing—and how they may be contributing—before discussing the team as a whole.	• Start with self reflection: "How did I contribute to our environment this week?" and "What is one behavior I could adjust to better support the team?"
Create conditions for candor with care	Honest input is more likely to surface when people believe the truth will be handled respectfully.	• Use caring language: • "Help me understand." "Say more." "What has been hard about this?" • Protect listening: One person speaks at a time. • Focus on understanding: "What I heard you say is . . . Did I get that right?"
Reframe mistakes as opportunities for improvement	Teams hide errors when mistakes feel like reputational threats. They learn faster when mistakes are treated as valuable information.	• Shift the default questions: From "Who did this?" to "What contributed to this?" and "What can we change so this does not happen again?" • Normalize learning language: "Mistakes happen—our job is to learn and prevent repeats."
Use a structured conversation format	Feedback feels safer when it is expected and structured, not improvised in moments of frustration.	• Use a clear format (e.g., Start–Stop–Continue, plus / delta, or "working / in the way / adjust"). • Use prompts that invite input from everyone, not only the most vocal participants. • Close by summarizing what was heard and what happens next.
Protect the conversation with clear boundaries	Psychological safety weakens quickly when ridicule, interruption, or retaliation are tolerated.	• State your non-negotiable norms: • "No ridicule." "No retaliation for raising issues." "Pause—can we reset how we are talking?" • Focus on behaviors and impact, not assumptions about intent.
Frame the conversation with practical safeguards	If the process asks for more openness than the team is ready to handle well, people may protect themselves rather than speak openly.	• If you anticipate people may hesitate to speak openly, use safeguards: • Anonymous input first, pairs or trios before the full-group discussion, or a neutral facilitator when power differences may make speaking openly difficult.

(*Continued*)

Table 4 (Continued)

Readiness Focus	*Why It Matters*	*Practical Moves*
Make action visible	People trust reflection when it leads somewhere.	• Convert insights into commitments. • Record actions in a visible place (a board/channel/log). • Clarify ownership and set a review date before closing.
Celebrate small wins and build credibility	Small wins build credibility and help people believe the effort is worth continuing.	• Ask "What is working that we want to keep?" • Name specific behaviors: "We caught that constraint early," "We clarified expectations before starting." • Make appreciation specific: what happened and why it mattered.
Have leaders model first	Leaders reduce social risk when they show humility and reflect openly on what they could do differently.	• The leader opens with a personal example of a time they failed to clarify, listen, or ask for help—and what it cost. • When someone raises a concern or disagrees, respond with curiosity before explaining or defending. • Reinforce early voice: "Thank you for surfacing that now—it gives us time to respond."

put in place so the team can reflect honestly and turn what surfaces into action. If you anticipate hierarchy, defensiveness, or "safe generalities," use the table to identify safeguards that may help.

A team is more likely to be ready when:

- People trust that they can speak honestly without being punished or dismissed.
- People can hear feedback and remain engaged.
- The purpose of reflection is clear, so the conversation stays grounded instead of drifting into complaint or confusion.
- Clear norms or facilitation mechanisms help keep the conversation respectful, focused, and productive.
- People believe that what gets surfaced will lead to action rather than disappear into a forgotten list.
- People are willing to reflect on their own contribution to how the team works.

Readiness, however, is not the finish line. It is what makes the next conversations possible. Once a team has enough readiness, it can begin turning reflection into action—surfacing what needs to change, deciding what to do next, and following through together.

7.2 From Readiness to Action

Readiness is what allows the action conversation to stay productive once difficult topics need to be addressed. Without that foundation, conversations drift into venting, people share "safe" feedback that sounds cooperative but avoids what actually needs to be said, and the team ends up with a list of ideas that no one turns into owned actions.

Action starts in the conversations where One Team takes shape—where people can surface what is real, hear each other, translate what they hear into commitments, and revisit them long enough for behavior to shift. In this chapter, action means running the loop:

Voice → Commitments → Follow-through → Learning → Improvement

Teams build this rhythm by creating space for voice while the work is underway. Simple, repeatable formats can make these conversations easier to begin—and easier to stay constructive once reality is on the table. These formats help teams:

- Lower the risk of speaking up by making the process transparent and expectations clear.
- Keep conversations grounded in observable work and behavior rather than personality judgments or vague complaints.
- Convert reflection into next steps so the conversation does not end with "good talk" and no change.

There are many ways to facilitate these conversations. Table 5 introduces three approaches that have been especially useful in our practice. Each creates a slightly different entry point into the same work: helping teams reflect honestly, identifying what matters, and moving toward shared action. The choice depends on context—how much trust already exists, how safe people feel speaking openly, how visible the issues are, and whether the team needs speed, structure, or added protection. Treat them as a menu of ideas to design something that fits your team. Your team's job is not to copy another team's solutions—it is to explore what works in your environment and build a rhythm you can sustain.

Sustained change rarely comes from one big declaration; it develops through repeated practice and visible progress. When a quieter voice speaks, when someone asks for help, when a leader receives feedback without defensiveness—those are small wins worth naming.

Facilitator Note

Before you dive into the conversation, explain the purpose of the conversation and what participants can expect. Make clear that the goal is to understand how the team is working, identify what needs attention, and agree on a few actions to try—not to assign blame or solve everything at once. When the purpose and expectations are unclear, people may default to familiar habits: staying vague, becoming defensive, blaming others, or rushing to solutions before the issue is fully understood.

Table 5 When to Use Each Approach

Conversation Format	*When to Use*
Start-Stop-Continue	The team is ready to openly name and discuss behaviors together.
Site Committees	You need an ongoing structure to create regular space for voice and keep follow-through visible.
Anonymous Input	Voice is uneven, hierarchy is strong, or you need protected input first.

7.2.1 *Start-Stop-Continue: Naming Patterns, Choosing the Next Moves*

The Start-Stop-Continue conversation is a simple way to help teams reflect on how they work together and surface opportunities for meaningful change. Treat this conversation as a *behavior design session*: the team names patterns, chooses a few shifts, and makes follow-through visible.

Through these conversations, the team surfaces behaviors that build safety and reliability or quietly erode them—and begins to design working agreements together. In this conversation, the team reflects on:

- What should we start doing because it would help us work better together?
- What should we stop doing because it creates friction, fear, waste, or breakdowns?
- What should we continue doing because it is already helping the team?

Reflection conversations can become unbalanced. Some focus only on problems and leave people discouraged. Others avoid talking about change altogether. Table 6 shows the prompts we often use to facilitate these conversations.

Table 6 Prompts to Keep the Conversation Focused

Start (to strengthen One Team)	*Stop (what gets in the way)*	*Continue (protect what is working)*
"What behavior would make it easier to speak up early?" "What would help us make and keep more reliable commitments?" "What would help reduce issues downstream"	"What do we do that makes people hesitate to tell the truth?" "What patterns contribute to broken promises" "What 'normal' behavior is costing us trust?"	"What do we do that makes it safer to ask questions?" "What do we do that helps commitments hold under pressure?" "What should we not lose as the team grows or changes?"

Guardrails for safety: Name behaviors, not people. Use examples, not labels.
Be aware: If the team stays in generalities ("communication needs work"), the output will not be actionable. If it turns into naming-and-shaming, psychological safety drops and people are less willing to speak up.

What makes this conversation powerful is the quality of the discussion it creates. It allows teams to talk not only about tasks or processes but also about how they experience one another. Issues like responsiveness, inclusion, reliability, respect, openness, learning, and speaking up can all surface here in a way that feels specific and actionable. Sources of friction that have remained unspoken, vague, or normalized can be named and discussed.

These conversations can:

- Give people a structured way to contribute ideas.
- Make room for appreciation and constructive feedback.
- Create a natural bridge from input to specific actions.

These sessions should not end with a long list and good intentions. Otherwise, even a thoughtful conversation can backfire: people leave having told the truth, but with no visible sign that their

Table 7 Steps to Facilitate a Start-Stop-Continue Conversation

Step	*Description*
Frame the purpose	• Open by making the purpose explicit: this is not about blaming people; it is about improving how we work together. Remind the team that the goal is to surface patterns, choose a few meaningful shifts, and make follow-through visible.
Collect input with appropriate safeguards	• Choose a format that best suits the team. Options include: • Individual reflection before group discussion. • Small groups before full-group sharing. • Anonymous input to gather input in advance. • These formats make it easier for more people to contribute without relying only on the loudest or most confident people.
Look for patterns	• Review the input together and group similar observations into a few shared patterns. • Avoid debating individual comments or trying to identify who said what. Instead, help the team notice where multiple comments point to the same issue, such as clarity, respect, voice, responsiveness, or follow-through.
Turn patterns into observable behaviors	• Move from broad themes to specific behaviors the team can actually practice. Shift from "communicate better" to: • "Pause at the end of handoff conversations to confirm scope, owner, and definition of done." • "Have the project manager join field walks to observe the work and discuss installation questions with the crews."
Start small and keep making progress	• Begin with two or three actions. Build from there rather than overcommitting at the outset. • Make each action specific and visible, for example: "We will START ending each coordination meeting by confirming who owns each action and when it is due. We will review how consistently we are doing this at next Friday's huddle."

input will shape what happens next. Over time, that teaches the team the wrong lesson—that speaking up is effort without return. Table 7 summarizes the steps we often follow to facilitate these conversations.

This exercise creates a shared language for behavior change. The implementation stories below illustrate how Start–Stop–Continue can produce different outputs across contexts. Teams X and Y are construction project teams working co-located; Team Z is a corporate team working virtually.

Implementation Story: Team X

After reviewing the craftworkers' team dynamics assessment results at Project X, one theme stood out immediately: a large portion of the workforce was unintentionally being left out of the project's main communication loop. At the time, more than half of the workforce were concrete workers, and the majority of them were Hispanic and primarily Spanish-speaking. Yet the weekly all-hands meeting—where the team shared key updates, expectations, and safety information—was conducted only in English. This meant that key information was not equally accessible to everyone attending the meeting.

Although Table 8 captured several actions the team discussed, they began by acting on two priorities:

- Including live bilingual translation during the weekly all-hands meeting.
- Creating a recognition program including both field and office participation.

They posted these commitments on a visible board on the project and revisited their status in the weekly coordination meetings, so the conversation turned into visible follow-through.

With the team's commitment and support, a bilingual field engineer began providing real-time Spanish interpretation during the all-hands meeting. This was not just a communication upgrade—it was a signal. This change sent a clear message to Spanish-speaking craftworkers, "this meeting includes you," and it reduced the friction of having to guess, rely on secondhand summaries, or stay silent to avoid embarrassment.

After those first few weeks, the team used what they learned to decide what to pull in next. They had named some "silent blockers" that kept people from speaking up (e.g., fear of errors, stigma around reporting near misses). To counter those patterns, the team made staff presence more visible and supportive in the field—inviting staff to join safety walks.

What changed next was subtle, then visible. Craftworkers who had previously stayed quiet started asking questions and clarifying expectations instead of filling gaps with assumptions. The tone of their meetings shifted from broadcast to dialogue—not because people suddenly became more outspoken but because the environment became more inclusive and therefore safer.

Table 8 Team X Start-Stop-Continue Themes (Co-located Project Team)

Start	*Stop*	*Continue*

• Using bilingual communication (English and Spanish) in all-hands meetings.
  • Live translation weekly; key visuals bilingual.
• Making recognition shared (field and office).
  • Recognition shared weekly, including at least one nomination by staff members.
• Inviting staff to join safety walks to build a shared understanding of field conditions and craft perspectives.
  • Rotate one to two staff members per walk.
• Forming an on-site safety committee to drive continuous improvement and strengthen relationships across trades.
  • Representative(s) from multiple trades and staff; monthly; track actions.
	• Treating mistakes as something to hide or fear.
	  • Replace with: "mistakes = learning opportunities."
	• Labeling near-miss reporting as "negative" instead of a learning opportunity.
	  • Replace with: "near misses = early risk detection," appreciate voice, learn, and improve.
	• Relying on the general contractor as the only communication bridge between trades.
	  • Replace with: direct trade-to-trade coordination.
		• Holding regular sessions with supervisors and general foremen to strengthen psychological safety.
		  • Review trends and focus on two to three targeted actions to improve as a team.
		• Reinforcing the recognition program through the "Doing It Right" campaign.
		  • Spotlight specific behaviors that contribute to the team (quality, safety, teamwork), not vague praise.
		• Sharing examples of craftworkers speaking up—so new team members see voice is welcomed and supported.
		  • Include one real story showing how speaking up led to support and action.

Implementation Story: Team Y

Team Y's conversation (documented in Table 9) surfaced a pattern that many large teams can relate to: the work was moving fast, but the team experience was uneven. Some voices dominated discussions. Others—especially the newer team members or people with less positional authority—held back. The group named it clearly: when discussions are dominated by the most experienced voices, valuable input can be lost, and others may find it harder to contribute.

Team Y started by redesigning how participation was structured—so participation would not be left to personality, title, or tenure. To keep the change manageable, they chose to begin with:

- Introducing structured turn-taking in coordination meetings.
- Replacing "we should" language with a visible commitment format (owner + date + follow-up).

Table 9 Team Y Start-Stop-Continue Themes (Large Co-located Project Team)

Start	*Stop*	*Continue*
Voice Using structured turn-taking so every voice is heard. * Inviting input broadly, do not default to "louder/most experienced voices." **Consistency and reliability** Putting a PE in the field daily to connect and observe work. * Making plans and decisions visible. Protecting time for quality: building capacity into the schedule. Clarifying core workflows and making them visible. **Connection and wellbeing** Creating regular opportunities for office and field teams to connect. Setting a cadence for check-ins. Normalizing healthy practices (breaks, vacations). **Lead by example** Increasing whole-team training (office + field). Recognizing good work consistently—while also addressing misses openly.	**Awareness and self-management** [SELF] Allowing frustration to shape how we respond when someone does not understand. [SELF] Treating role-based exceptions to respectful behavior (e.g., yelling) as "normal." * **Discipline** Using vague "we should" language instead of clear commitments (owner + date + follow-up). Holding meetings without a clear purpose, agenda, expectations, or follow-through. Not spending enough time in the field or regularly walking the site with superintendents.	**Connection** Hosting jobsite events (family day, craft lunch). Weekly scope-sharing meetings that create space for everyone to contribute. **Appreciation** [SELF] Leading with kindness. Recognizing and reinforcing speaking up. Celebrating quality and safety wins (shout-outs). Offering training to continue expanding capabilities. **Consistency** Partnering with field teams to get ahead of issues and make speaking up easier. Asking "why" when expectations are not met. Following practical prevention habits (e.g., pre-pour photos). Bringing critical safety topics into all-hands meetings. **Lead by example** Treating mistakes as opportunities and repairing with kindness. Keeping direct and anonymous ways to share feedback—every voice counts.

"*" Indicates prioritized commitments, marking the beginning point of follow-up conversations.

As the team introduced more structured participation, they began to see issues surface earlier and assumptions get tested sooner. They made follow-through visible by assigning a process keeper to capture commitments live and review them monthly.

In parallel, the team named the interpersonal habits that could quietly undo the process—letting frustration leak into tone and tolerating role-based exceptions to respect (yelling, dismissive behavior). They made one simple "Stop" boundary explicit: no yelling or dismissive behavior gets a pass—regardless of role.

Team Y reinforced these shifts through routines that strengthened connection and appreciation. They continued practices that were already working—weekly meetings that allow every trade to speak, craft lunches, and events that build camaraderie (family days, happy hours). But they added a more deliberate focus: making "speaking up" a behavior worth repeating. Leaders committed to recognizing good work publicly and privately, celebrating quality and safety shout-outs, and explicitly appreciating those who raised issues early. They also preserved multiple feedback channels—including anonymous options—so people had more than one way to contribute when direct voice still felt risky.

Team Y did not treat speaking up as a personality issue or respect as a vague value. They treated both as something the team could intentionally shape. They redesigned meetings so voice was more evenly distributed, redesigned commitments so follow-through was easier to see, and clarified behavioral boundaries so respect did not depend on role, stress, or seniority.

Implementation Story: Team Z

Team Z shows what the same conversation can unlock in a corporate team distributed across regions. Distance can make misalignment and isolation harder to notice, and building connection requires even more intention when people do not share the same physical space. Team Z's initial conversation, summarized in Table 10, focused on connection, trust, and team health.

One of the first things Team Z recognized was that it is easier to mistake silence for alignment, especially in remote work where cameras are often turned off. If someone is overloaded, frustrated, or confused, you will not notice it in a hallway—and you may not hear it in a meeting unless you create a place for it. They decided to start with a practical move to address this: assessing team health intentionally and periodically. They committed to using a team health assessment as an annual reset, paired with regular check-ins, to understand how people were doing. To reinforce connection beyond the screen, they also redesigned their annual in-person meeting around relationship-building and alignment—not just getting work done.

Equally important, Team Z prioritized celebrating both big and small wins as a way to reinforce progress, strengthen belonging, and make contributions visible across distance. This aligned with what was already working: emphasizing care for people and sustaining trust-building activities that keep communication open. The team built recognition into standing meetings so showing appreciation became part of the team's regular rhythm, not dependent on one leader remembering to do it. They designed their actions so that the connection did not depend on proximity.

Taken together, these three cases show how one consistent process can produce priorities that reflect each team's context. Team X focused on inclusion and language access, Team Y

Table 10 Team Z Start-Stop-Continue Themes (Distributed Corporate Team)

Theme	*Start*	*Stop*	*Continue*
Team health and care	Running a consistent team health assessment. Getting to know each team member better.		Emphasizing taking care of people. Using activities to strengthen trust and communication.
Recognition	Intentionally celebrating big and small wins as a team.	Focusing only on the what is not working.	
Vulnerability and belonging	Sharing openly about strengths and areas for improvement.	Working through challenges in isolation. Judging each other.	Making space for people to share what they are working on.
Connection	Checking in on team members' personal successes and challenges.		Collaborating as a team and developing one another's capabilities. Hosting an annual in-person meeting for team development.
Voice channels	Encouraging peer feedback. Offering multiple ways to give and receive feedback.		Speaking up and embracing vulnerability to build trust.
Capability building	Hosting a book club, starting with Reliable Promises.		

focused on meeting voice and commitment discipline, and Team Z focused on connection and trust across distance. Across all three, the conversation served the same purpose: it helped teams name what was getting in the way, choose a manageable set of next moves, assign ownership, and revisit those moves as they worked toward a healthier way of working.

7.2.2 *Ask the Question: What Would Make Speaking Up Safer?*

Sometimes the most honest starting point is not a live conversation at all but rather an invitation that feels safe enough to accept.

We often begin by asking teams this question:

What would make you feel safer to speak up?

Most often, we offer an anonymous path to share responses. Anonymous input can help reveal patterns that the team may not yet be ready to name aloud. But over time, the aim is to build enough safety and structure so that more of those conversations can happen directly, respectfully, and productively.

This question is not the end of the work. It is an entry point. It helps teams surface what people need before asking them to speak more openly, and it gives leaders a practical way to respond with visible changes instead of assumptions.

In one case study, we posed this question to 169 participants (approximately 90% craftworkers and 10% staff) and received 130 suggestions. Participants described specific conditions that would make speaking up less risky and more worthwhile. The responses reflected a very practical view of psychological safety: people want to be able to speak up about hazards, mistakes, and uncertainty—and have that voice met with respect, protection, and action.

Facilitator Note (How to Use This Question)

- Collect: ask the question in a way that makes it easier for people to respond honestly.
- Cluster group responses into themes and choose where to begin.
- Commit: choose two to three actions to begin (behavior + owner + where it lives + review date).
- Close the loop: share back: "Here is what we heard. Here is what we are changing now. Here is what we are not changing yet (and why). Here is when we will revisit."
- Repeat: Set a cadence to revisit, "What feels safer now? What still makes speaking up challenging?"

Figure 47 What Makes People Feel Safe—Case Study Themes.

As shown in Figure 47, the most common theme was leader accessibility and respectful interaction. Responses pointed to wanting a closer connection and approachability—a "1 on 1 chat with my super [superintendent]," and "more involvement of the supervisor with us." They also emphasized the importance of dignity in how leaders communicate: "it is not what you say but how you say it," calling for coaching rather than "shouting or bad words," and simply, "when I talk, please listen!"

A second clear pattern was the desire for safe channels to raise concerns. This points to a practical reality: even when people care deeply about safety, some situations still feel socially risky. Anonymous mechanisms are not just for convenience—they are a way to reduce fear, conflict, or embarrassment while keeping information flowing.

Their responses also show two closely related expectations that shape whether people keep speaking up: a non-punitive response and job security, and follow-through / being heard. Participants asked for assurance like "to not get punished or sent to a different job" and "no discrimination for [reporting] accidents." They also emphasized the need to see that voice leads somewhere: "action must be taken when someone speaks up, not just listening and doing nothing," and "seeing that suggestions and concerns are being addressed." These themes are less about "encouraging voice" and more about credibility: people are watching whether speaking up is both safe and worth it.

Recognition also emerged as an important theme. Responses pointed to a desire for leaders to acknowledge workers' contributions and highlight what was going well, not only what needed improvement. This kind of reinforcement helps shape what people believe is valued on the team. When leaders celebrate effort, improvement, safe choices, and responsible speaking up, they reinforce that these behaviors matter and are worth repeating.

Overall, the results highlighted several conditions participants associated with speaking up: accessible and respectful leaders, protected reporting channels, capability-building, non-punitive responses, and visible follow-through. People wanted reassurance that speaking up would not trigger punishment, and they wanted leaders—especially supervisors—to be close enough and respectful enough that questions and concerns could be raised in real time.

This question can be your action trigger: ask, listen, pick a few moves, and make the response visible. The response does not need to be big; it needs to be specific, visible, and revisited. Once teams begin to see that protected input leads to visible change, they are better positioned for the next move: a standing mechanism that keeps learning and follow-through alive over time.

7.2.3 Site Committees: Seeing the Work, Hearing the People

Regardless of how a team surfaces priorities (a survey, Start–Stop–Continue, a retrospective, a painful breakdown, or a strategic reset), one challenge remains: good intentions decay when the system does not support them. People return to delivery pressure, meetings fill up, and the "we agreed" list becomes invisible. A site committee is one practical response to that decay: it gives the team a standing place to see the work, hear the people, and close the loop consistently enough that improvement becomes normal work—not a special event.

A committee, as we mean it here, is not a governance body, an audit group, or a place where management "reviews" the field. It is a representative working group—and a standing forum for follow-through—designed to go see the work and the people, convert observations into action, and keep commitments and learning visible, owned, and revisited once the day-to-day pressure returns, instead of letting them fade into "normal work." A committee combines three design features:

- **Representation:** Members reflect the system (functions, roles, trades, regions, or interfaces), so the committee sees what the leadership alone can miss.
- **Routine:** Recurring touchpoints create reliability—people know there is a next moment to check-in and continue the conversation.
- **Safeguards for psychological safety:** The format reduces interpersonal risk by turning observations into shared learning and next steps.

This kind of structure helps protect teams from a very common form of deterioration: the normalization of preventable problems. Without a place to regularly surface concerns, teams often adapt to poor coordination, uneven respect, missed commitments, and recurring frustrations until those patterns start to feel inevitable. A committee interrupts that by making reflection and response part of how the team operates, not something saved for moments of failure.

How the committee functions:

1. It follows a predictable rhythm:

   Cadence: a steady routine (e.g., monthly walks paired with a short weekly check-in).
   Focus: one or two focus areas per walk (avoid trying to inspect everything).
   Consistency: the same prompts each time, so patterns can be tracked and discussed over time.

2 It has a "go see" approach to foster learning:

Looking for wins and drifts: what is working, what is slipping, what changed since last time.
Grounding in observation: what we saw / where we saw it / why it matters.
Engaging with people doing the work: short conversations that surface friction early and respectfully.

3 It has cross-boundary learning as a design feature:

Bringing different parts of the system together: including craftworkers (multiple trades) + project staff so the committee sees what any one group misses.
Creating a shared understanding: walking the work together across crews and observing areas and activities beyond each person's own scope.
Learning across crew boundaries: sharing observations and perspectives so people can learn from how other crews work, understand how their scopes affect one another, and identify opportunities to improve together.

4 It has psychological safety guardrails that protect credibility:

It is safe enough to name what is real (no ridicule, no retaliation, no blaming the messenger).
It is worth speaking up (visible follow-through, clear updates, closed loops).

A committee's value is not the walk itself—it is what the team learns and does with what it sees and hears. Outputs must be shared, trackable, and revisited:

- An observation log (what was seen, where, and why it matters).
- A prioritized action list with action owners and due dates.
- A record of patterns and trends over time (what keeps recurring, what is improving, what is getting worse).
- A feedback loop to the broader team.

Instead of waiting for frustration to accumulate until someone raises it in a tense moment, the committee becomes a standing place where feedback, reflection, and learning can happen in a more regular rhythm. That rhythm matters under pressure. In demanding environments, teams are more likely to improve when they create and protect a mechanism for noticing and adjusting while the work is underway, rather than waiting for the workload to ease before reflecting and adjusting.

Implementation Story: Site Safety Committee

Team A had already invested in understanding the human side of safe work through a field survey and direct conversations. One finding stood out: workers were far more willing to speak up within their own crew than across crews. In the survey results, 43 of 64 respondents strongly agreed they would speak up when they saw someone on their crew doing something unsafe—but only 24 strongly agreed they would speak up when the unsafe act was happening on another crew.

This gap is not a technical problem. It is a trust and relationship problem. The team responded with a structural move: they formed a safety committee with one representative from each trade, intentionally mixing experience levels. A field engineer served as the convener at the beginning—setting up the meetings, selecting the walk focus areas, and starting the conversation—without turning the committee into a hierarchy.

Each walk was designed to identify both (1) wins worth naming—so the team could repeat them and (2) areas that needed support before they became incidents, rework, or frustration.

Walk Location		Who did you talk to?	
OVERVIEW			
	Question:	**Answer**	
1	What is being done right in this area?		
2	Are the crews cleaning as they go?		
3	Is material easily moveable? Is there enough space to work safely?		
4	How is the morale on the job? Who should we recognize?		
5	Any near misses on this crew this week?		

PICK 1 TOPIC BELOW AND GET INTO MORE DETAIL				
	YES	NO	INSPECTION POINT	COMMENTS
1			**PPE:** Are workers wearing personal protective equipment?	
2			**ACCESS:** Are exits and stairways clear?	
3			**ORGANIZATION:** Are construction materials stored properly?	
4			**ELECTRICAL:** Are cords, plugs, and temporary power in good condition, protected, and properly grounded?	
5			**FIRE PROTECTION:** Are extinguishers available where needed, accessible, and within inspection date?	
6			**OVERHEAD WORK:** Are tools/materials secured (tethered as needed) and are drop zones/exclusion areas clearly set?	
7			**FIRST AID:** Is the first aid kit stocked and accessible?	
8			**COMMUNICATION:** Are required signs posted, visible, and understood (hazards, routes, restricted areas)?	
9			**EQUIPMENT:** Is equipment in safe operating condition (inspected/tagged)?	
10			**FALL PROTECTION:** Are workers using proper fall protection?	
HAVE A CONVERSATION. DOCUMENT IT.				
Recognize a specific contribution you observed during the walk and explain why it mattered.				
Are there any hurdles or issues we can help you take care of?				

Figure 48 Handout Used by Safety Committee Members During the Site Walk.

Figure 48 shows the handout that the safety committee members used during the walk. That handout provided a common structure for what members observed, the questions they asked, and the information they captured. It helped focus the walk on both field conditions and conversations with the people doing the work. The project leadership then reviewed a summary of the completed handouts during the weekly coordination meeting to drive action and follow-through.

Figure 49 shows a portion of the committee walk report—a color-coded tracking log that organized observations by work zone and observation category. The numbers across the top

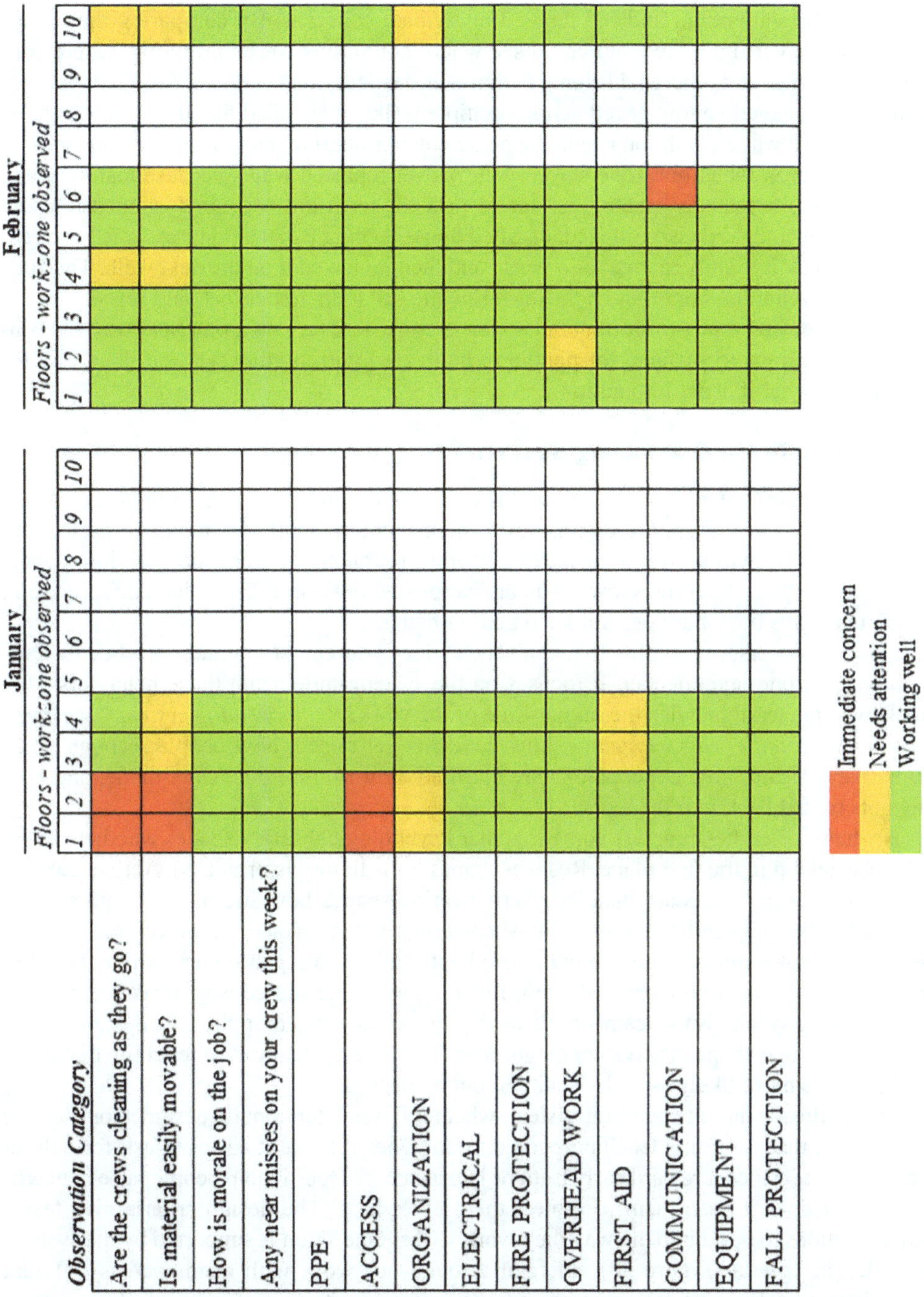

Figure 49 Craft Safety Walk Tracking Log.

identify the zones observed, while each row represents a condition or topic the committee reviewed. In addition to the color ratings, the log included notes capturing committee members' observations and insights in each zone. Green indicated conditions working well, yellow identified areas needing attention, and red flagged immediate concerns. By comparing the ratings across zones and over time, the team could see where conditions were improving, where concerns were recurring, and where additional action was needed.

When patterns stayed yellow or red across multiple walks, it signaled that the issue was not a one-off mistake—it was a condition needing a better countermeasure, more coordination, or more support. For instance, when one zone stayed yellow over repeated walks because materials and housekeeping were repeatedly creating an access risk, the team did not just document it again. They adjusted how materials were staged, clarified housekeeping expectations, assigned one representative to check it at shift change for a week, and then reviewed it on the next walk. The zone improved—but even more importantly, the team saw the full loop: notice, act, and revisit.

Across all three conversation formats, the idea is consistent: create a practical way for concerns and observations to surface, for people to be treated with dignity when it does, and for the team to turn what it hears into action.

7.3 The One Team Operating System

When teams struggle to work well together, it is often not because they reject the idea of working as One Team. More often, the day-to-day system unintentionally rewards self-protection: move fast, do not be wrong, do not ask, do not bring problems forward, do not slow people down. Over time, these patterns show up as late surprises, rework, difficult handoffs, burnout, and a team that stays busy but does not keep getting better.

In previous chapters, we explored specific behaviors you can strengthen to work as One. This section goes one level deeper. It focuses on the system underneath those behaviors—the repeatable way the team handles the human side of the work. *By "operating system," we mean the built-in way a team works together*: how concerns get raised, how people respond when something hard is said, how expectations are clarified, how commitments are made, and how learning gets folded back into the work.

This is where the earlier chapters come together Psychological safety shapes whether people feel able to speak up in the first place. Respect shapes how dignity is protected. Active learning shapes how misses and wins are handled. Active caring shapes how strain, need, and support are noticed. Speaking up and active listening shape how truth is surfaced and received. Reliable promises shape how commitments are made and kept. The operating system is where these behaviors stop being separate lessons and begin functioning as one shared way of working.

If the operating system is the team's built-in way of working together, then the design criteria are the conditions that shape that system on purpose. They are the features of team life that make healthy behaviors more likely—not by accident but by design.

Every team already has an operating system, whether it was intentionally designed or not. The question is what that system is teaching people to do. Does it make it easier to ask for help or easier to stay quiet? Does it reward early truth or late cleanup? Does it help people raise concerns with dignity, or does it push them to protect themselves first? The design criteria give teams practical conditions to build into the way they work so that One Team is supported by the system.

These design criteria (Figure 50) emerged through our work with teams across different settings, where we observed recurring conditions that made it easier for people to speak up earlier, respond constructively, coordinate more reliably, and learn together. Certain conditions appeared repeatedly: expectations were clear, dignity was protected, questions were welcomed, responses to concerns were constructive, and learning was made visible instead of assumed. The

Figure 50 One Team Design Criteria.

criteria below reflect those recurring patterns. They are not meant to be a rigid formula, but a practical set of conditions for intentionally building a healthier way of working together.

Design Criterion 1: Be Intentional

One Team does not just "happen" because people are talented or well-meaning. Teams need to intentionally create conditions that support healthy ways of working—especially when the work gets fast, stressful, or messy. Without that intentionality, the system can default to patterns rewarded in the moment: speed over clarity, silence over questions, politeness over truth, and "just push through" over learning. Intentionality means you stop leaving team health and behavior to chance. You make it part of how the team runs the work—regular, visible, and protected.

What to operationalize:

- Pay attention to changes and patterns in how people experience the team, using assessments, check-ins, direct observation, and feedback conversations—and respond to the conditions helping or hindering healthy ways of working.

- Build regular, protected opportunities for reflection and listening into the team rhythm so these conversations still happen when the work gets busy.
- Name the "why" upfront so people understand why the team is intentionally taking time to talk about how they work together.
- These conversations are part of the work—not something reserved for when problems arise.
- Keep the team's shared purpose and priorities visible, especially when roles, crews, or functions have competing needs, so decisions consider what is best for the team as a whole.
- Create regular opportunities for people across roles, crews, or functions to plan, reflect, and solve problems together rather than relying on coordination to happen informally.
- Convert input into action by tying what you hear to specific changes, clear ownership, and a point to revisit progress.

Design Criterion 2: Make Dignity Non-Negotiable

When pressure rises, *tone becomes the hidden leader*. If people expect impatience, harshness, or embarrassment, they will protect themselves—and voice shrinks to whoever feels safest talking. In One Team terms, this is permission-setting: the way leaders respond under stress teaches the team what is "safe enough" to do next. A calm, respectful response gives people permission to ask, clarify, admit uncertainty, and raise concerns early. A sharp tone, ridicule, or messages such as "move fast and do not be wrong" send the opposite message: protect yourself, stay quiet, and do not take risks.

What to operationalize:

- Treat people with kindness and dignity at all times—including when mistakes are made, expectations are missed, or difficult issues need to be addressed.
- Acknowledge people's contributions and efforts, not only what needs to be corrected or improved.
- Pay attention to how people are experiencing the team and one another. Look for indications that someone may be excluded, dismissed, unsupported, or disconnected, and check in rather than assuming what they are experiencing.
- Listen to understand, especially when someone raises a concern, disagrees, or shares feedback. Give them the attention and space to explain what they mean before responding.
- Pay particular attention to how you communicate under stress. Pressure is not a reason to become impatient, dismissive, sarcastic, or disrespectful.
- Repair moments when dignity is compromised. If someone is dismissed, embarrassed, interrupted, or treated disrespectfully, acknowledge it and reset the interaction rather than simply moving on.

Design Criterion 3: Make Asking for Help the Safest Path

Needing help is not the problem. Problems grow when people feel they have to hide that need and continue working without the clarification, support, or resources they need. When the fastest path is to stay quiet and figure it out alone, teams usually pay for it later. In One Team, help-seeking is treated as a normal part of doing the work, not as a sign of incompetence.

What to operationalize:

- Set the expectation that asking questions and requesting help are part of doing the work well, not signs of incompetence.
- Make it clear how and where people can go for help and encourage them to ask before uncertainty becomes harder to address.
- Look for opportunities to support one another. When someone signals uncertainty, names a challenge, or identifies something getting in the way, offer help or ask what support would be useful.
- Practice simple language people can use: "I'm not clear yet—can you walk me through what 'done' looks like?" or "I need some help with ___ before I move forward."
- Respond constructively when someone asks for help by providing the clarification, support, or resources they need—or helping them find the right person.
- Reinforce help-seeking when you see it: "Thanks for asking early—that gave us a chance to work through it together."

Design Criterion 4: Respond in Ways That Invite Voice

Your response is the real policy. Even in teams that say, "speak up," people pay attention to what happens when someone actually raises an issue. Constructive responses encourage people to keep contributing; dismissive or disproportionate responses can make them more hesitant—or make speaking up feel pointless.

What to operationalize:

- Acknowledge the person for speaking up, especially when the concern may have been difficult to raise.
- Pause before reacting, particularly when the information is unexpected, uncomfortable, or challenges a decision already made.
- Ask questions to understand what the person is raising before deciding how to respond.
- Respond proportionately. Take the concern seriously without dismissing it or escalating it unnecessarily. Avoid extremes:
  - Under-reacting (little or no reaction) → people stop bothering.
  - Over-reacting (escalating the issue before understanding it) → people stop risking it.
- Be clear about what happens next: what will be acted on, what needs more information, and what may not change—and why.
- Close the loop so people know what happened with what they raised.

Design Criterion 5: Build Protected Pathways for Voice

Many conversations unintentionally reward speed (the quickest speakers), status, or comfort speaking in groups. One Team cannot depend on perfect timing or confident personalities. It needs multiple pathways for people to contribute to lower the social risk of voice. Not every concern belongs in the same setting. Depending on the issue and situation, people may be ready to speak in the room, need time to think, or prefer a smaller or more protected channel. Protected pathways do not weaken candor; they widen access to it.

What to operationalize:

- Give people different ways to contribute depending on the situation—for example, speaking in the group, discussing in a smaller setting, writing first, or responding anonymously.
- Choose the pathway based on how difficult or risky it may feel to raise the issue. More sensitive concerns may need a more protected way to surface first.
- Create reflection time before group discussion when people may need time to organize their thoughts before speaking.
- Use structured participation when needed so the conversation is not driven only by the people who speak first or most often.
- When an issue or decision affects multiple roles or crews, intentionally invite input from the people whose work will be affected—not only those leading the conversation or making the decision.
- Use anonymous input as a bridge when needed, while continuing to build the conditions for more direct conversation over time.

Design Criterion 6: Make Expectations Explicit

Many breakdowns that surface during execution begin earlier—with unclear expectations, fuzzy handoffs, and different interpretations of what was agreed. If roles are unclear, help can feel like interference. If "done" is undefined, a promise becomes guesswork. If decisions are not documented, people might remember different agreements. One Team members coordinate more reliably because "what we mean" is made explicit early. However, understanding what is expected does not necessarily mean people are ready or able to commit to it. Clarity also requires room to negotiate before committing. When people feel they must say "yes" quickly—without fully understanding scope, constraints, or capacity—commitments become guesses. One Team strengthens when teams pause at the right moments to clarify what is needed, plan the work together, and identify issues early enough to prevent surprises downstream.

What to operationalize:

- Clarify what success looks like before work begins.
- Before making decisions or commitments, ask who else will be affected and what needs to be coordinated with them.
- Clarify handoffs across roles and crews: who needs what, from whom, and what needs to be true for the next person or team to succeed.
- Surface constraints, capacity, and anything else that could affect the work before making a commitment.
- Before moving forward, ask what could get in the way and adjust the plan when needed.
- Make it acceptable to pause before committing when more information or clarification is needed.
- Use counterproposals when the original request cannot realistically be met rather than giving an unreliable "yes."
- Confirm shared understanding of decisions, expectations, and next steps rather than assuming everyone interpreted them the same way.
- Make important decisions and agreements visible so people have a common reference point.

Design Criterion 7: Make Learning Visible and Normal

Learning becomes part of the team's way of working when it is expected, regular, and visible—not reserved for moments when something breaks. One Team learns in two directions: by leveraging what is already working, and by responding well when something does not hold. *Breakdowns will happen. The difference is whether the team hides them, blames them on someone, or uses them to improve.* When a commitment is at risk, the team surfaces it early, renegotiates, and protects downstream teams from surprise. One Team is not the absence of breakdowns—it is the presence of a reliable learning habit that turns misses into prevention and wins into repeatable practice.

What to operationalize:

- Create space for learning and adjustment: "We would rather learn early and adjust than discover a bigger problem later."
- Treat surfacing problems as a contribution to the team; naming what is getting in the way creates an opportunity to learn and adjust.
- Encourage people to raise commitments that are at risk early, explain what changed, and propose a next step.
- Make experimentation manageable by defining a clear scope, what the team wants to learn, and review points.
- Review both misses and successes: "What happened? What did we learn? What should we repeat or change next time?"
- Create opportunities for people to learn across roles and crews by reviewing work together, sharing what they see, and understanding how different parts of the work affect one another.
- Make learning visible by capturing what changed and revisiting whether the change is working.

Design Criterion 8: Coach Behaviors Consistently

Healthy team behaviors must be developed rather than assumed. One Team scales when behaviors are named, practiced, coached, and reinforced like any other capability. Teams should not rely on a one-time workshop or expect people simply to pick up these behaviors by watching others. If the team wants people to raise concerns well, respond well, ask for help early, listen actively, and respond to misses respectfully, those behaviors need to be taught, modeled, and revisited in the normal flow of work.

What to operationalize:

- Talk openly about the behaviors that support One Team during onboarding and throughout the work—for example, how to raise a concern, respond to one, ask for help, or repair after a miss.
- Build leaders' capability to model and coach behaviors such as listening, responding constructively, and handling difficult conversations.
- Give people opportunities to practice these behaviors, not only hear or read about them.
- Coach behaviors in the moment with specific feedback about what worked and what could be done differently.
- Encourage team members to reinforce and respectfully coach one another so healthy team behaviors are not dependent on leaders alone.

- Reinforce behaviors when you see them so people know what is worth repeating.
- Do not wait for a major breakdown to coach. Use everyday interactions as opportunities to strengthen the way the team works together.

Design Criterion 9: Engage Fully

Attention is respect in action. When people experience distracted listening or constant rushing, they learn that their input is low priority—even if no one says so directly. One Team requires presence. Questions, concerns, and ideas are not interruptions to the work; they can help the team understand what is happening, clarify uncertainty, and get the work right the first time. When someone speaks up, engaging fully means giving that moment the attention it deserves rather than rushing past it to keep the work moving.

What to operationalize:

- Reduce avoidable distractions so you can stay present and engaged in the conversation.
- Give people your full attention when they raise a concern, ask for help, question an assumption, or share something that needs to be understood.
- Show that you are listening by pausing, asking questions, and confirming what you understood before responding or moving on.
- Make space for questions and clarification before closing a discussion or making a decision.
- Resist the urge to rush through moments of uncertainty or disagreement simply to keep the work moving.

When teams build these criteria into how they work, One Team stops being only an aspiration and becomes something people can experience in everyday interactions. People do not have to wonder whether asking, raising, or admitting uncertainty will backfire—they begin to see that those behaviors are expected, supported, and useful.

Once a team starts operating differently, it will feel different. Some people will test the boundary. Some will resist the new clarity. Some will experience the shift as "slower" at first because the team is no longer skipping the conversations that could prevent problems later. That friction does not mean that this effort is failing. It often means that the old operating system is being challenged.

In the next section, we turn to what that friction often looks like in practice—so teams do not mistake normal growth tension for a sign that they should stop.

7.4 Venturing into New Territory: What to Expect

New territory is where teams either grow or retreat into old patterns. If you are bringing psychological safety and behavioral dynamics into the open, expect and lean into discomfort. This discomfort is not evidence that you are doing something wrong. It is evidence that you are touching the invisible rules many teams have used to survive: do not look inexperienced, do not slow things down, do not challenge the plan, and do not be the squeaky wheel. Growth often begins exactly there—at the point where the team starts noticing and challenging the habits they once treated as normal.

Once a team starts working more intentionally on how team members relate, coordinate, and learn together, the process rarely feels smooth at first. It often feels awkward, slower, less certain, and more emotionally charged than expected. People may wonder whether the conversation is helping or simply making things harder. The goal is not to treat all discomfort as failure, but to understand what is causing it and keep the process respectful and constructive.

Early Reactions When Teams Begin Reflecting Openly

Many teams are not used to talking about how they work together while the work is still underway. People may get quiet, joke, intellectualize the topic, or speak in generalities instead of naming specific behaviors. These reactions may reflect uncertainty rather than resistance. They can emerge as teams move from an "execute and deliver" mode to a "plan and learn" mode. And a learning mode can feel surprisingly vulnerable because it asks people to slow down, reflect, and say out loud what usually stays underneath the surface.

That vulnerability does not always show up in obvious ways. Defensiveness may sound like strategy: "We do not have time for this." Frustration may sound like certainty: "That is just how it is." Lack of trust may sound like self-reliance: "I can do this myself." Exhaustion may sound like cynicism: "We have tried this before; nothing changes."

Participation may also be uneven at first. Some people may engage quickly, while others may need more time or may first watch how the team responds when something uncomfortable is raised. Silence can have many meanings; it may reflect a need for time, uncertainty about the process, or concern about whether speaking up will be received with kindness. A healthier team is not one in which everyone participates in the same way. It is one in which, over time, more people feel able to contribute, see that their input is welcomed, and believe that speaking up can make a difference.

Facilitator Note

Normalize the process without lowering the standard.

> "If this feels awkward, that is expected. We are talking about behaviors and practicing skills that may not usually be discussed this openly."

Name patterns, not people.

> "I'm hearing a concern about time and follow-through. Let's make that explicit and design the conversation so we leave with actions we will actually revisit."

Do not force vulnerability. Build evidence.

> "Not everyone has to say everything right away. What matters is that we keep making it safer and more useful to contribute over time."

Change Is Slower and Less Linear Than Teams Expect

Once teams begin naming challenges, people often want to see improvement quickly. That desire is understandable. But behavioral and relational change often moves more slowly than insight. A team may have a meaningful conversation and still find that coordination habits, tone, follow-through, or responsiveness improve only gradually. Old patterns may reappear, progress may be uneven, and some changes may be easier to see than others. That gap between insight and visible change can create frustration. People may start wondering whether the conversations are making a difference.

Some teams abandon the process because they expected insight to produce immediate behavioral change. This is where consistency matters. Teams do not become healthier because they had one good discussion. They become healthier because they keep returning to what they said mattered, keep practicing different responses, and keep following through long enough for the new behavioral patterns to take hold.

Old patterns may come back, especially when deadlines tighten, coordination gets messy, or people feel overloaded. A team that was becoming more open may suddenly get short with one another. A leader who was listening well may become more directive under stress. Someone who had started raising concerns may go quiet again. This does not necessarily mean the process has failed. It often means pressure is revealing which habits are truly changing and which still need support. Setbacks can provide useful information. They can show which new behaviors are beginning to hold and which still need more practice, support, or structure.

Facilitator Note

Name the pace honestly.

> "We may understand the issue before we are good at doing something different about it. That is normal. The goal is consistent practice with visible follow-through."

Treat regression as data, not defeat.

> "What changed around us that made the old pattern more likely to return? What support or structure was missing?"

Misconceptions That Stall Buy-In

Some people may misunderstand the purpose of this work. They may think psychological safety means being nice all the time, lowering standards, or avoiding accountability. Others may assume it is soft, extra, or disconnected from performance. If those misconceptions take hold, the work can lose credibility before people have actually experienced its value.

Working as One Team does not eliminate challenges; it helps teams work through them more productively and deal with reality together. Teams under pressure often reject what they think will slow them down. They need to see that this work is not separate from delivery. It is one way the team protects delivery from the hidden costs of silence, confusion, resentment, and late surprises.

Facilitator Note

Clarify the purpose in practical terms.

> "This is not about lowering the bar. It is about helping us work through problems earlier, more honestly, and with less waste."

Making Sense of What Surfaces

As teams create more space for honest input, they may hear more than they expected. Concerns that seemed minor may reveal deeper patterns. Small frustrations may connect to larger issues of role clarity, respect, trust, workload, or leadership response. Sometimes the team opens the door expecting a few adjustments and instead finds a more honest picture of how people have been experiencing the work.

This can feel destabilizing at first. People may think, "Are things worse than we thought?" Not necessarily. The team may simply be seeing a fuller picture. What is surfacing now may have been present for a long time; it just was not visible or discussable before.

Hearing more clearly is progress. But it can also create a new challenge: deciding what to do with what has surfaced. Teams do not need to work on everything at once. What they need is the discipline to notice patterns, prioritize what matters most, and begin where focused action can create the most meaningful shift.

> **Facilitator Note**
>
> Help the team pace itself.
>
> "We do not have to work on everything at once. Hearing more clearly is progress. Our next job is to decide where to begin."

None of this means the team must handle every challenge in the same way. What it does mean is that teams benefit from knowing how to interpret what they are experiencing and how to respond without overreacting, giving up, or slipping back into old assumptions. The next section focuses on how to do that with more intention and shared ownership.

7.4.1 Be Upfront—This Matters!

To get your team engaged in this process, be clear about why this is worth their time. Do not assume the value is obvious to everyone. Say it plainly and connect it to what teams experience people hesitate to speak up, ask for help, clarify expectations, or raise concerns: missed risks, missed opportunities, rework, resentment, and burnout. But do not stop there—because the cost of not working as a team is not only what goes wrong. It is also what never shows up. *Name what you are protecting: the work and the people delivering it.*

Be clear that this work is not separate from performance. How people speak up, ask for help, clarify expectations, learn, and coordinate affects both the quality of the work and people's experience of doing it.

Be upfront: this work is about how teams perform well and stay healthy. It protects people, protects the work, and creates the conditions for the team to improve together. Be honest that this may feel uncomfortable at first. You are asking people to speak more openly than they may be used to—not to make things harder but to improve how the team works together.

A Simple "Be Upfront" Script (Use as Written or Adapt)

We are doing this because how we show up for each other as a team matters just as much as the work itself.

When people do not feel safe to speak up, teams miss opportunities. Risks stay hidden, frustrations build, coordination breaks down, and the same problems keep showing up in different forms. Our people end up carrying the burden, and both people and performance pay the price.

When people do feel safe to speak up, the opposite becomes possible. We surface issues earlier, learn faster, coordinate better, and make reliable commitments. The work becomes clearer, and the team gets stronger—not just because problems are solved but because people solve them together.

This conversation is not about putting anyone on the spot. It is about improving how we work as a team. The goal is to reflect honestly, identify what will help us work better together, and leave with commitments we will revisit.

Once the importance is clear, the next question is how to structure the conversation so more people can contribute. If the format favors speed, seniority, or comfort speaking spontaneously in a group, you may get a narrow slice of reality. If it gives people time to think, protects dignity, and asks for examples, it can make broader participation more likely.

7.4.2 A Team Effort

Once the team understands why this matters, the next challenge is making sure the conversation does not only belongs to the loudest, most senior, or most confident voices. Design conversations so that more people have a meaningful way to contribute. When participation is broad, issues can surface earlier, assumptions can be tested, and the team gains a fuller picture of what is happening.

Design for Participation

Design the conversation so more people can contribute safely and specifically.

- Write first, then share. Give everyone thought-time before airtime so the conversation is not dominated by the fastest speaker.
- Use small groups before full group when stakes are high (pairs → table groups → full room).
- Use structured turn-taking so that everyone has an opportunity to contribute.
- Convert themes into observable behaviors. Do not leave with "let's communicate better." Leave with actions people can practice, such as:
  - "If a request is unclear, then we ask clarifying questions before saying yes."
  - "If a commitment becomes at risk, we raise it with a proposal."

Make the Conversation Real and Simple

Keep the conversation grounded in the work people actually do.

- Start with something specific to anchor the conversation in a real moment: an RFI that came too late, repeated rework, a near miss, or a meeting where people left with different understandings of the decision.
- Debrief for behavior: "What did we notice? What helped voice? What shut it down? What will we try next time?"
- Pick one skill to practice (listening, speaking up, clarifying, negotiating). Keep it small and continue building on it.
- Repeat in the real rhythm of work (huddles, handoffs, weekly coordination) so practice becomes normal. Practice develops new behaviors; consistent repetition turns them into lasting habits.

Get Leaders' Commitment Early

These conversations work best when people with the most influence show up fully. If leaders treat the process as optional, the team may do the same. Leaders can set expectations through their own behavior:

- Model the participation you expect—for example, by asking clarifying questions, receiving feedback with curiosity rather than defensiveness, and helping close loops.
- Ask leaders to go first in showing the kind of openness they want from others—by acknowledging something they may have missed, a concern they did not see early enough, or a way they could have supported the team better.
- Reinforce speaking up by recognizing it as a valuable contribution to the team.
- Make follow-through visible. When people raise concerns, leaders should help the team see what will be acted on, what needs more thought, and what happens next.

Designing conversations this way makes broader participation more likely and gives the team a fuller picture of the work. More voices can bring earlier warning signs, different perspectives, and better information for deciding what to change.

7.4.3 Lessons Moving Forward

As teams move toward becoming One Team, the experience of working together may begin to change. Not because the job gets easy or the pressure disappears but because people stop carrying uncertainty, frustration, and risk alone. One participant in our studies put it simply:

"We deserve to feel good where we work."

That shift begins when questions are treated as prevention, not incompetence. Clarification becomes a sign of care, not weakness. Helping and speaking up become normal moves, not interruptions.

Teams may also notice an important change in how people collaborate across roles and trades: the shift from "my work" to "our work." These conversations do not just improve individual confidence; they strengthen cross-role and cross-trade collaboration as helping, clarifying, and speaking up become normal parts of getting the work done.

In healthy teams, people do not have to choose between being honest and being safe. They speak up early, coordinate more reliably, and repair quickly when something goes wrong, without blame or humiliation. When teams ground this work in clear, repeatable practices—how we ask questions, how we respond, how we align before work, and how we treat each other under stress—people leave with more than insight. They begin to experience a different way of working together; one that feels safer, clearer, and more genuinely One Team.

One Team, Many Paths

Teams can build One Team behaviors in ways that fit their people, work, and circumstances. The core principles remain the same, but the practices that bring them to life depend on your people, your history, and how your team operates. A one-size-fits-all program rarely fits every team because:

- Teams begin in different places.
- Teams operate under different contexts and pressures.

That is why "One Team" is not a rigid formula. It is a shared way of working that your team has to design in a way that fits its reality: what feels "safe" in a small co-located crew may feel risky in a large cross-functional team; what works in a steady phase may break under a schedule crunch. So, treat this book as a design guide, not a prescription. Your job is to build a way of working that fits your team and holds up in difficult times.

Exploring what works for your team requires paying attention to the voice of its members, experimenting with different approaches, and adjusting as you learn. Rather than generating a long to-do list, choose a few practices, put them into practice, review what changed, and adjust.

Identify your starting point[1]:

If speaking up feels risky: start with protection and low-risk formats.

Anonymous input first.
Small-group discussions before full group.
An explicit non-retaliation boundary.
One visible follow-through action early ("you said / we did").

If coordination is messy: start with clarity and reliability.

Conditions of satisfaction at handoffs.
Define "done" and decision rights.
Short commitment reviews ("what did we promise / what changed / what do we need?").

If capability is a bottleneck: start with practice and coaching.

Role modeling and examples.
Training tied to real tasks.
Scripts for asking questions, surfacing concerns, and making counteroffers.
Peer learning ("how do you do this safely and efficiently?").

One Team grows through learning. Not every strategy will work right away. Some experiments will fall flat; others will work better than expected. What matters is the loop that the team runs together:

Plan (how we will operate as One Team)

→ Do (practice it in everyday work)
→ Check (what are we experiencing, and what needs attention?)
→ Act (adjust together and continue)[2]

Teams sustain One Team practices by using this cycle repeatedly—not as a one-time intervention but as a regular way of learning and adjusting together. This might mean tightening a practice (clearer conditions of satisfaction in handoffs), replacing one (swapping long retrospectives for quick after-action reviews), or adding a new one that matches current realities. Adapting the practice does not mean losing direction; it means responding to what the team is learning.

How Does One Team Endure Over Time?

One Team endures when it stops being an intention and becomes a shared way of operating—something the team can point to and say, "this is how we work here." It lasts when people can see that way of working in the team's daily life: in how meetings are run, how concerns are received, how commitments are tracked, how help is requested, and how the team responds when pressure rises. Over time, this way of operating together becomes culture: not because people say, "We are One Team," but because the team keeps practicing the behaviors that make "One Team" true.

The specific practices may vary, but the aim stays constant: Start small. Make it visible. Revisit it. Be consistent—so the team stays healthy. Projects change. People come and go. New pressures emerge. What worked in one phase may need to be tightened, simplified, or adapted in the next. One Team endures when people notice drift and recalibrate together, when commitments are revisited instead of forgotten, when new team members are intentionally brought into the way of working, and when setbacks become opportunities for learning and repair. No two teams will build their rhythm in exactly the same way. But every healthy team needs one.

In the next chapter, we hear directly from leaders who have taken this work personally and operationally—leaders who show how they create the conditions for psychological safety in everyday work. Through their stories, you will see how leaders make voice safer, dignity more visible, and learning more usable—so that "we" becomes more real across the team.

Notes

1 The Team Dynamics assessment introduced in Chapter 1 provides a baseline for understanding how the team is currently working together, helping you identify patterns, gaps, and strengths. Use the conversation guides and exercises throughout the book to explore those areas more deeply.

2 In *The New Economics*, Deming describes PDSA as a learning cycle in which teams plan a change, make a prediction, test it, study the results against the prediction, and act on what they learn.

Chapter 8

Guide the Way

Creating the Conditions

Across earlier chapters, we explored what psychological safety looks like in lived behavior: how people experience respect, how learning stays active, how caring translates into real support, how speaking up is met with genuine listening, and how reliable commitments are made and kept. This chapter turns to the role leaders play in creating the conditions for those behaviors. It is one thing to understand psychological safety. It is another to support it consistently through deadlines, pressure, conflict, and uncertainty. That leadership work matters because psychological safety is where One Team begins.

People watch closely how leaders respond when someone challenges a plan, admits a mistake, asks a "basic" question, or flags a risk that could slow the schedule. These moments do not just shape the outcome; they shape how the outcome was reached. Over time, the team learns—often without anyone saying it out loud—whether it is safe to speak up and whether speaking up will result in a meaningful response.

Leadership shapes whether psychological safety becomes a lived reality, where voice is normal, truth can be acted on, and learning is part of how the team works—or remains a fragile hope, where people speak only when the perceived consequences feel low.

This is part of the leader's role in making One Team possible: creating conditions where contributing to the team feels both safe and worthwhile. In One Team, people do not have to choose between protecting themselves and protecting the work, because belonging is not conditional on being right. People can disagree, clarify, interrupt work, and still remain "in."

We close the book by examining how leaders help create and sustain these conditions. As you read the stories that follow, pay attention to what these leaders consistently do. They do not rely on charisma, personality, or perfect words. They make speaking up easier through clear permissions, repeatable check-ins, feedback that builds rather than bruises, and interactions that protect dignity. They intervene when responses, behaviors, or working conditions begin to discourage voice. They model vulnerability without losing accountability. Most importantly, they show through their responses that speaking up leads somewhere—toward clarity, support, action, or a better decision. The following leaders show how these principles can be practiced in different roles and settings. Prepare to be inspired!

8.1 Leaders Who Make It Real

The leaders featured here do not just ask people to speak up and expect it to happen automatically. They create conditions that support and reinforce speaking up. In doing so, they help teams work less like disconnected individuals protecting their own ground and more like One Team solving real problems together.

DOI: 10.1201/9781003734864-8

A note on format: the stories that follow are shared in the leaders' own voices and written in the first person. Throughout these stories, Paz, Nick, Stephen, and Jack speak in the first person—describing what they did, what they learned, and how those experiences shaped their leadership.

Paz Arroyo

Project Manager
DPR Construction

Leadership and psychological safety go hand in hand. You cannot be an effective leader if you do not help create a psychologically safe environment for your team, and you cannot assume it is already there—especially in construction, where every project brings together a new mix of people, pressures, and relationships.

I have worked in the construction industry my whole career, starting in Chile, working for a lean consulting firm implementing the Last Planner System, and then in a construction company that built tunnels for mining projects. I earned a PhD at UC Berkeley and now work at DPR Construction in the USA. When Sulyn asked me to write about psychological safety from a leader's perspective, I agreed, eager to support this important book. I have participated in many of Sulyn's research projects, followed the interventions she has led at our firm, and co-authored some of her papers. Even so, I found writing about psychological safety challenging. Every time I tried to start writing, I found myself intimidated by the task and the responsibility of giving you something insightful to read. So I want to begin with a disclaimer: I do not have all the answers; I still make mistakes. I am and will continue to learn throughout my life. But I have learned a great deal from environments where psychological safety was absent, and from the practices that have helped me build it more intentionally as a leader.

As a leader, I think about this work in three areas:

1. Taking care of yourself so you can learn, grow, and develop your leadership skills and vision in a way that is compatible with what the organization needs, and what you are good at and passionate about.
2. Taking care of the people you directly lead—people whose performance and development you are responsible for supporting.

3. Influencing people over whom you do not have direct authority but whose support you need to achieve a shared vision.

Understand the Environment and Take Care of Yourself

To be a great leader, you must respect people's perspectives, circumstances, and right to autonomy. You must actively listen to people's concerns and empathize. You must speak up and share what you see and what you know is relevant to succeeding in a project, even if that means sharing your mistakes. You must show that you care about others by providing support and guidance and acting on what you agreed to do. You must make and expect reliable promises. You must be willing to learn from each other. Unfortunately, I have learned from personal experience that some managers in the construction industry are poor leaders; they are poor listeners, make unreliable promises, and do not show the respect people need. Many have never been fortunate enough to learn the skills that foster psychological safety. As I said, I did not have these skills when I started, but I am still eagerly learning.

One of the first lessons I learned is that leaders cannot create healthy conditions for others if they are not paying attention to the conditions they are creating for themselves. When I first became a manager in 2007, I was in Chile. I had just finished my master's degree and suddenly found myself leading a team of young engineers who audited management systems on construction projects and reported back to the CEO of a midsize general contractor. I was ambitious, energetic, and eager to prove myself. At that stage of my career, I thought leadership meant working harder than everyone else: arriving first, leaving last, always being available, always having an answer.

That mindset shaped how I treated my team. If I needed information late at night, I called them. If the monthly report was due, we all stayed until it was done. I paid little attention to their personal lives or limits. I simply assumed they were available and that this was what commitment looked like. The company itself reinforced that mindset. It was hierarchical, tense, and highly focused on producing a cohesive story for leadership.

One time, after a visit to one of the projects at a large copper mine, I noticed the team was not working well, and the project leader was not leading the planning meetings. He was, in fact, playing on his computer in a corner of the room, totally disengaged. I attended all their regular meetings, including one with the owner, where he made many significant scope changes that were not documented and joked that a handshake should be enough. Later, when I walked the field, I talked to the excavator operator, who told me they were making him rework every day because the layout was incorrect, and that it was impossible to be productive.

When I came back from the visit, I made a report and crossed paths with one of the company's directors, who asked me about the project visit . . . so I shared what I saw. Minutes later, the CEO called me into his office. I was reprimanded for sharing too much; how could I be so sure of what I saw? He asked me to share bad news little by little next time, or, even better, not share at all—and let the problems show up in the reports once we were actually losing money. For the record, the company lost a lot of money on the project and ended up with several claims against the owner.

As you can tell from this story, I was working in an environment in which speaking up was not welcome and respect for people was not the norm. I was so focused on building my reputation as a hard worker that I was not paying enough attention to my teammates' personal needs—or to my own wellbeing. I was excited to see the projects, learn from them, and share best practices. However, I could feel that people did not have much space to learn or ask questions;

there was only one way, set from the top down. I was so focused on building a reputation as a hard worker that I was not taking care of myself; I was not eating or exercising well. I was not taking care of my team. I am thankful this happened to me early in my career, and I knew deep down that I did not want to work in that environment ever again.

Over the years, I have had many opportunities to learn new leadership skills and to learn about the importance of consistently taking care of myself. Becoming a mother has taught me so much about caring for people, and I am now more flexible and better able to empathize with those who need to care for others at home or have other personal needs. I also learned the importance of taking care of myself to be able to care for others.

After the COVID-19 pandemic, I was not feeling like myself; my energy levels were down, and, like many others, I decided to dig deeper. I went to a year-long coaching certification program with New Venture West, which helped me understand my own motivations and what I needed in my life. I realized how much of my drive had been shaped by overachievement—not always by what truly mattered to me but by wanting to look good or prove myself. That realization changed how I lead. Now I am much more deliberate about how I spend my time. I make sure I have time to sleep, eat well, exercise, be with my family, and be creative. I enjoy cross-stitch and weaving regularly. Those things are not distractions from leadership; they help make me capable of it. *Only after taking care of myself can I be a good leader for others.*

Taking Care of the People You Directly Lead

A different lesson came when I had to help someone rethink her career path. She was excellent at coordinating people. She was empathetic, warm, and brought humor and lightness into our meetings. But she was also leading an initiative to develop a new company quality process that required input from multiple experts, and she was getting stuck. What seemed to be holding her back was not lack of effort or intelligence. It was the discomfort of receiving contradictory input from different subject-matter experts.

As her coach, I had a responsibility to speak up. But speaking up was only part of that responsibility; I also needed to give the feedback with clarity, honesty, and care. We had a respectful conversation in which I helped her see a pattern: Once she had something in mind, every differing opinion felt frustrating and destabilizing. That insight mattered. Instead of privately carrying the burden of reconciling everyone's opinions on her own, she began asking for direction more openly. She brought the conflicting voices together, named the contradictions clearly, and led the group toward a collective decision. The work moved forward because she no longer felt she had to hold the uncertainty by herself.

That experience opened the door to deeper conversations. What was she passionate about? What kind of work energized her? Around that same time, I learned about an open role on another team that needed someone skilled at coordinating diverse stakeholder requirements. I shared it with her. She was excited because the role was more connected to what she had studied, but she was also worried about the travel demands and what that would mean with small children at home. So, we talked through it. She applied, got the job, earned a promotion, lined up family support, and negotiated the travel. For me, that was a strong reminder that taking care of people is not just about helping them succeed in the task they are doing now. It is also about helping them see possibilities and career paths they may not have considered.

A couple of training courses that helped me develop better skills to work with others are WEST (working effectively in small teams) and Learning to Navigate Moods by Fernando Flores and Gloria Flores. They helped me pay closer attention not only to what people were saying but also to what might be underneath their words. Leaders often react to behavior without understanding what is fueling it. When you learn to notice the mood underneath—frustration, anxiety, resignation, fear—you can respond in a way that helps people move forward instead of shutting down.

Influencing the People You Do Not Have Authority Over

At DPR Construction, I worked in Quality Corporate Services from 2018 to 2025. I led the Culture of Quality objective team for the last two years, and during that time, I led a group tasked with revitalizing quality culture in their Business Units, but I did not have direct authority over them. I was not their manager, so I had to lead primarily through relationship, trust, and clarity.

My role was to help the remote team prioritize initiatives, create an environment where people felt comfortable sharing ideas before they were fully developed, coordinate efforts to avoid duplicating work across the company, and listen to the frustrations and challenges they were facing. An important lesson learned was to set aside time to develop relationships with each culture of quality champion. Each business unit faced different challenges and needs, and each person had a different background: some were superintendents, some were project managers, and others held other regional roles. Some held a full-time support role, some were on a project, and this was a passion project for them. Understanding their capacity, motivations, and challenges was my starting point.

Before we could make meaningful progress, we had to build a shared vision. We spent a significant portion of our meetings aligning on what "culture of quality" actually meant—what belonged inside that vision and what did not. At times, that felt slow. One of my biggest challenges was documenting that shared view and publishing it clearly in our internal operations framework. But I also knew that without that alignment, we would keep pulling in different directions. Once we had a clearer shared direction, the team was able to prioritize initiatives more effectively, share progress openly, and collaborate across business units in ways we had not before.

I now believe leaders need to be intentional about creating and maintaining psychological safety throughout the life of a team. People come and go, roles change, and team dynamics evolve.

I recently started a new role in 2026. I am a senior project manager in an Integrated Form of Agreement (IFOA) megaproject. My role involves implementing a lean production system strategy. Again, I am in a role where influence matters as much as authority. My first priority has been to get to know people. We have an incredible team of designers, builders, engineers, and consultants who were brought in early to collaborate, and we have an owner who is very supportive of lean practices, including the Last Planner System. But support alone does not create trust. New teams still have to learn how to work together.

That is why we are being intentional about the conditions we are creating. We are trying many strategies: "getting to know you" moments in the big room, onboarding processes that help people enter the team with more clarity, and education around the Last Planner System and reliable promises. These are not side activities. They are part of how a team learns to trust, coordinate, and create value together.

I want to leave you with this message: Never assume psychological safety is already there. Build the relationships that allow people to open up. Create conditions where sharing incomplete ideas feels possible. Be willing to show vulnerability, admit when you do not know the way, and acknowledge your mistakes. Fostering psychological safety is an ongoing journey. Best of luck with yours!

Nick Loughrin

Corporate Director of Project Delivery Services, The Boldt Company

Psychological safety is something I was exposed to long before I had a name for it. Growing up, whether it was at home or in sports, there was always this sense of equality and openness. Coaches and family members encouraged everyone to speak up, and there was always room for opinions and choices based on our input. Nobody was forced to do anything, and I think that is where my initial understanding of a safe environment began.

But it was not until I was part of Boldt's Leadership Academy back in 2016 that I really started hearing the term psychological safety more frequently. I remember watching Amy Edmondson's TED Talk about the subject, and it clicked for me. It gave language to something I had already felt but had not yet named. It helped me connect the dots between the kind of openness I had experienced growing up and the kind of culture we were trying to build at Boldt. Psychological safety became something that I could more consciously incorporate into how I lead. I understand that psychological safety, in its simplest form, is an environment where people feel safe to speak up. For us at Boldt, it really ties into our company's culture of respect, which was embedded in Lean practices long before we ever formally talked about psychological safety.

At Boldt, one of the clearest ways psychological safety has always shown up is by empowering people to stop work if something does not feel right. This is especially important on job sites, where the safety of our workers is always the top priority. It is something we stress on every job site:

"If it does not feel right, everyone is empowered to stop the work!"

In the early stages of talking about psychological safety, we made sure everyone knew they had the authority to stop work when something did not feel safe or right. This idea evolved into something even deeper over time. As I became more involved in leadership, I realized the importance of setting the tone in meetings and creating that space where people felt safe expressing themselves. With greater responsibility came a deeper understanding: I realized that creating an environment where people felt psychologically safe was not just about having the right policies in place; it was about consistently modeling the behaviors that sustain a safe environment.

As I grew in my leadership role, I started learning how to coach others to create that same kind of environment. That transition—moving from doing it myself to coaching others on how to do it—has been one of the hardest yet most rewarding parts of my journey. It is one thing to create a safe space in your own interactions. It is another to help other leaders do the same in a way that feels authentic, repeatable, and strong under pressure. That is still something I continue to refine.

I recently had a conversation with a new team member, who is very enthusiastic and eager to make an impact. This individual is full of energy and driven to prove their value. They were involved in a proposal for a new project, and the feedback from the project team was that their approach was a bit too directive. There were many instances of "I did this," "I did that," and "We need to do it this way," which came off as overbearing.

It was a tricky moment because I did not want to shut down the very energy that made this person promising. I just needed to help redirect it. I spent a weekend thinking about how to approach the conversation. The key, I realized, was to stay open, empathetic, and specific. I needed to help this person see that collaboration is not the opposite of leadership; it is often what makes leadership effective. That conversation reminded me that psychological safety is built in moments like these. It is built when feedback is honest without being bruising, and when people leave a hard conversation clearer and more supported rather than smaller.

I have been working hard on improving how I give feedback. Early in my career, I was really focused on the "what needs to be fixed" side of things. I would see something that could be improved, and I would dive right in with suggestions or do it myself. But what I have learned is that feedback must be balanced. You cannot just focus on the things that need improvement. You must recognize what is going well too because naming what is working reinforces what "good" looks like and helps create the trust people need in order to hear what also needs to change. And it is not just about giving feedback, it is also about being open to receiving it. I try to make it clear to my team that I'm just as open to feedback as I hope they are. *Feedback is a two-way street.*

To ensure regular, meaningful feedback, I have implemented weekly check-ins with my team. We talk about their successes and roadblocks. I want to know what went well, what is working in their lives, both personal and professional. Then we dive into any challenges they are facing. I always ask, "How can I help?" It is an opportunity for them to give me feedback, too. These consistent check-ins also help build the relationship needed for harder conversations. When people know you care about them as people—not just as performers—it becomes easier to talk about what is not working and what needs to improve. And that is not just a one-time thing; it is an ongoing effort. I have found that when I take the time to get to know my team on a personal level and show that I care, they are more willing to share their ideas and concerns.

Psychological safety is crucial in the construction industry. Construction is a high-pressure environment, and if people do not feel safe to speak up, you are going to see issues. This might not show up immediately, but it will in the long run. I have seen firsthand how projects go south when the culture is not one where people feel comfortable raising concerns or asking questions. Even when the project on paper is "making money," if people are not having a good experience, or they do not feel respected and valued, the project is a failure in my book. A project like this would have lost many opportunities to improve the bottom line and the chances of the people on the project wanting to stay and do it again are not likely. But, when psychological safety is present, people are more engaged, they share their ideas, and the team works better together. That kind of environment does not just feel better—it performs better.

Building psychological safety is not always easy. At times, you will encounter resistance, especially if the leadership on a project is not aligned with those values or they do not fully embrace this concept themselves. I have worked with leaders who did not understand the importance of creating a psychologically safe environment, and that can be a major roadblock. In those situations, it is crucial to model the behavior you want to see. It can be tough, but it is important to stay true to your values and keep pushing for that culture of safety and openness.

If you find yourself in a toxic environment, sometimes the best solution is to remove yourself from that situation. I have been fortunate not to face that many times, but I have seen it happen to others. When that happens, I think about the saying "*change the people or change the people*". Sometimes leaders have to make harder calls to protect the culture. Coaching should come first whenever possible, but there are situations where mindset or behavior does not change, and protecting the team requires a different decision.

One program that really promoted psychological safety on a project was the *Bambino Program* we implemented at the Akron Children's Hospital project (Figure 51). Inspired by the idea of recognizing people doing great things, the Bambino Program was a simple but powerful way to encourage the behaviors we wanted to see on the job. Team members could nominate their peers for things like safety, quality, or production improvements. These nominations were displayed on a board in the lunchroom, and the individuals who were recognized received a custom sticker, which they proudly displayed on their hard hats. It was not a costly or complex program; it was just a way to celebrate the good things happening on the job and recognize those who were contributing to the project's success. Participation became broad, and the program helped create an environment in which people saw that their contributions were noticed.

When people feel that their contributions are recognized, they are more likely to engage and contribute even more. This creates a cycle of reinforcement that builds trust and encourages everyone to continue sharing their ideas.

Figure 51 Bambino Program Site Poster (Courtesy of Boldt).

Over the years, initiatives like the Bambino Program have inspired our current company-wide recognition program, Starfish Moments. It is an app-based recognition tool that allows team members to nominate others who have gone above and beyond in demonstrating Boldt's virtues and values. The program is based on the Starfish Parable, which emphasizes the importance of making a difference, even if it is just for one person. This Parable really captures an idea at the heart of meaningful recognition: even a single action that helps one person matters. The story goes like this: A young boy is walking along a beach where thousands of starfish have been washed up during a storm. He begins picking them up one by one and throwing them back into the ocean. An older man watches him and says, "You cannot save all these starfish. What difference does it make?" The boy picks up another starfish, throws it back into the sea, and says, "I made a difference for that one."

Programs like Bambino and Starfish Moments make appreciation visible and reinforce the behaviors the organization wants to see repeated. When you recognize someone for their contributions, it creates a ripple effect and encourages others to do the same.

For leaders who are just starting to think about psychological safety, my advice is to start by really understanding the problem. Ask questions, listen to your team, and do not jump to conclusions. And most importantly, lead by example. It is one thing to talk about psychological safety; it is another thing to actually foster it consistently in everyday interactions. Leaders set the tone, when leaders do not practice the behaviors they ask of others, their efforts to build psychological safety lose credibility.

As for organizations, they need to support leaders by providing the right resources and structures for mentorship and coaching. Training is important, and learning deepens through experience, reflection, coaching, and mentoring. It is about creating a culture where leaders can continuously grow and help others grow, too. Also, we need to ensure that leaders across the company are aligned and supportive of the same values. That is how we are going to scale psychological safety across the industry.

Looking ahead, I hope that psychological safety becomes the norm in the construction industry. It is already taking root in some areas, like Integrated Project Delivery (IPD) projects, but we have a long way to go. My hope is that we will keep pushing forward, showing the industry that psychologically safe environments lead to better outcomes. The more we talk about it, the more we will see change. And when it becomes a norm, we will have safer, higher-quality, and more productive teams where everyone is empowered to contribute and make a difference.

Stephen Terni

Environmental Health and Safety (EHS) Operations Integration Leader, DPR Construction

I've come to realize that psychological safety is at the heart of everything we do, whether it is building a construction project, leading a team, or simply working with others. For me, in our industry [construction], it is easy to think of safety in terms of physical safety, but as I have learned over the years, psychological safety is just as important. It is not just about making sure people are not physically hurt; it is about creating an environment where every person can thrive and feel that they can speak up.

My journey toward understanding psychological safety in its formal sense started after the George Floyd incident in 2020, during a period of profound change and uncertainty. This was when I was collaborating with a group of industry peers, and we began diving into what it meant to be inclusive and how psychological safety fit into that picture. It was around this time, with the added layer of the COVID-19 pandemic and the challenges of transitioning to virtual work, that I began to see more clearly how deeply psychological safety shapes team culture and how essential it is for people to feel able to bring their whole selves to the table.

I realized that every successful team of which I have been a part had one thing in common: people felt psychologically safe. They felt safe expressing their thoughts, asking questions, and even disagreeing without fear of judgment. To me today, psychological safety is *THE foundation* for how we build successful relationships, solve problems, and navigate the complexities of the job. I did not always understand it in those terms, but I think my journey has been one of discovering how critical it is to foster an environment where people feel safe to speak up, share ideas, talk about mistakes, and be vulnerable. As a leader, I have learned that psychological safety is something I have to actively foster and maintain.

Start With Vulnerability

I used to think that I needed to have all the answers, that as a leader, I had to be the one who could solve every problem, and I could not afford to show weakness. One of the biggest shifts in my leadership style has been learning to be more vulnerable. But over time, I have realized that leadership is about being open and allowing others to contribute. People need to see that you are human, that you make mistakes, and that it is okay not to have all the answers. That is where it begins, creating a space where *it is okay not to be perfect.* Showing vulnerability is one of the most powerful things a leader can do. When you show that you are willing to admit when you do not know something or when you make a mistake, it signals to your team that it is okay for them to do the same.

One of the most memorable moments I recall about the importance of psychological safety comes from a project where things did not go quite as planned. We were working on a large office building, and the team was struggling to meet deadlines. The Project Executive (PX) decided to introduce a new system for communicating commitments and progress with the owner, hoping it would help streamline our process. The PX gave the team specific instructions about what should be included in the weekly reports to the owner without fully understanding the systems that the project managers were using to generate those reports. As a result, the instructions did not align with the project managers' understanding of how their information systems worked.

When he introduced the proposed changes in a large meeting, no one spoke up, no one questioned it. The project managers, despite not fully understanding the intent of the request, did not want to contradict the PX in front of everyone, and they were afraid that asking questions might make them seem not a "team player" or uncooperative. So, they went away, worked on the reports, and a few days later discovered that what they had created was not what the PX wanted. This led to a lot of wasted time and rework. This lesson stuck with me, and I have made it a point to never let silence in a meeting be interpreted as agreement. *Silence is not alignment, it is often fear, confusion, or a lack of understanding.*

Looking back, I realize that the team was not able to speak up because the environment was not right for that kind of conversation. In a large meeting, it is much harder to ask for clarification, especially when there are power dynamics at play. That experience reinforced for me that leaders do not just need to invite voice; they need to design contexts where voice has a real chance of happening.

A Dynamic Concept That Requires Deliberate Efforts

Psychological safety is something you have to work on. I have been on teams where the level of psychological safety was low. This drains energy from the team. People hold back, they do not share ideas, and they do not engage fully. I have seen people on those teams leave; or worse, they stay but are not really present. They stopped performing at their best because they did not feel like their input mattered. And that is when I realized that the lack of psychological safety is a problem that needs to be addressed quickly.

In one instance, I was part of a team where the leadership style did not align with mine, and the team environment made it difficult for me to learn, build new relationships, and contribute fully. That experience was draining and became emotionally exhausting. I spent so much time thinking about how to navigate the team dynamics that I could not focus on solving the actual problems at hand. That is when I realized that when teams lack psychological safety, they do not perform as well. There is too much mental energy spent on interpreting personal dynamics instead of moving forward on the project.

However, when there is psychological safety, everything changes. I have seen teams that embrace vulnerability and openness thrive. On one large project, the team was facing some issues around coordination, and the decision-makers were having trouble communicating the right information to the craftworkers. Decisions were delayed because of lack of clarity, and ultimately, the craft teams did not have the information they needed to proceed with their work. Team members were working in silos, and as a result, the project was behind schedule.

To address this, the team changed the structure of the conversation. Instead of letting decisions move through long chains of communication, they brought decision-makers directly to the field on a weekly basis. The project created a smaller working group that included project managers, architects, engineers, and foremen so issues could be discussed directly with the people doing the work. That change mattered. Problems were solved faster, questions were raised earlier, and feedback from the craftworkers became part of the decision-making process rather than something discovered too late. The result was not just better coordination. People felt heard and respected. That increased ownership, commitment, and pride in the work. For me, that was a powerful reminder that psychological safety is not abstract. It shows up in whether information moves, whether people can clarify, and whether the right voices are close enough to the problem to help solve it.

This experience reinforced my belief that leaders must be proactive in fostering psychological safety. You have to create the right environment for the team to thrive. Also, psychological safety is not something that just happens overnight. It takes time, patience, and consistency. There will always be challenges along the way. Sometimes, you have to navigate different leadership styles, cultural differences, or team dynamics. But as a leader, you have to be aware of these challenges and actively work to address them. And always remember that this is a continual journey, it is not a one-time fix. The best teams are those that are constantly learning, improving, and supporting each other. The best teams have breakdowns as well, and they respond through a commitment to each other to get back on track.

From my experiences, I have identified several practical ways that leaders can foster psychological safety within their teams. These ideas are rooted in my own journey, as well as my observations of what has worked (and what has not) over the years:

- Understand your team dynamics and build self-awareness: People show up differently—some speak quickly, others need space. Effective leaders pay attention to these patterns and help the team reflect on how their behaviors affect others.
- Model vulnerability by admitting uncertainty and mistakes: Leaders do not need to appear certain at all times. When you say what you do not know or take responsibility for a mistake, you show that learning matters more than having all the answers. This makes it easier for others to speak honestly, ask for help, and take responsible risks.
- Design meetings for voice and clarification: Silence does not equal agreement. Create intentional space for clarification—through smaller groups, written input, one-on-one follow-ups, or explicit pauses to ask, "What might we be missing?"
- Make feedback normal and multidirectional: Create regular opportunities for feedback to flow in all directions. Team members should feel as safe giving feedback to you as receiving it from you. When feedback becomes routine rather than rare, it feels developmental—not threatening.
- Listen actively and visibly: Listening is more than hearing words—it is demonstrating that input has been understood and considered, explaining how it informed the decision, and closing the loop when it cannot be acted on. When people feel genuinely heard, they are more likely to speak up again. Active listening reinforces that voice is worthwhile.
- Pair grace with accountability: Treat mistakes as opportunities to learn but do not leave expectations vague. People thrive when they are supported and clear about what matters.

Organizations like DPR have done a lot to support leaders in fostering psychological safety. One thing I really appreciate is the company's commitment to asking where employees are at and creating space for those conversations. We have resource groups, social responsibility calls, and other initiatives that help us connect and share our experiences. But it is also about creating opportunities for leadership growth—making sure that people have opportunities to develop, prepare for, and grow into leadership roles.

As a leader, I'm committed to constantly learning how to create a more psychologically safe environment for my team. We cannot assume the work is ever "done"; we have to keep paying attention, learning, and making adjustments. In the end, we are all human: we make mistakes, learn, and grow together.

Jack Poindexter

Northwest Regional Leader and Leadership Team Member, DPR Construction

When I began my career in construction, psychological safety was not even on my radar. I was focused on the work, meeting deadlines, and dealing with the daily pressures of the job. Although

I cared about the emotional wellbeing of the teams I was leading, I cannot say it went beyond trying to ensure people looked satisfied with their work and happy to be a part of the team.

I first heard about psychological safety when Sulyn visited our job site in 2018. At that time, I did not fully grasp what it meant. She was conducting her PhD research and introduced me to the concept in the context of quality, explaining that people needed to feel safe enough to speak up when they saw a quality issue to ensure we were all doing our best work. That initial introduction sparked something that grew over time. As I took on more leadership roles, the true power of psychological safety started to unfold for me. When I stepped into a leadership role overseeing self-perform work (SPW) for DPR Construction's Northwest region, the full importance of psychological safety hit me.

At the time, I was still figuring out what it meant to be a leader for our craftworkers as well as our staff, and how I could create an environment where my team felt safe speaking up. In that role, I was now directly supporting nearly 750 DPR craftworkers. The more I led, the more I realized that psychological safety was not separate from respect; it was one of the clearest ways people experienced it. When people feel respected, they are more willing to raise concerns, ask questions, admit mistakes, and speak honestly about what is not working. When they do not feel respected, they hold back—and in construction, that silence can carry serious consequences for our people, our projects, and our company.

A pivotal moment in my journey with psychological safety happened on a project where I was walking the job site, just doing my regular check-ins. I made it part of my routine to stop and talk to our skilled craftspeople to see how things are going and if they need anything. On one occasion, a worker shared that a superintendent had threatened him with termination over what I understood to be a relatively minor issue. It was immediately clear to me that the response had been out of proportion and warranted follow-up. After looking into the situation, I addressed it with the project leaders and reinforced our expectations for treating our craft workforce with dignity, especially in the everyday moments when frustration runs high. What stayed with me was how exposed and disposable a person may feel when a workplace interaction appears to put their livelihood at risk. A moment like that can make a jobsite feel less like a team and more like a place where one wrong move comes at a high cost.

This conversation helped me realize how vulnerable people can feel in this environment. When they feel threatened, they are less likely to speak up or voice concerns, even when it is crucial to do so. It was an eye-opening moment that solidified my understanding of psychological safety. I was deeply concerned by what I heard, and I immediately addressed the issue with project leaders with a clear message: That is not how we speak to any of our teammates. That experience, combined with my responsibilities as a leader, pushed me to think about how I could foster a genuinely psychologically safe environment for everyone on the team.

From Intention to Action

One of the first things I realized in my pursuit of creating a psychologically safe environment was that it is more than the words we use; it is also about the actions we take and the role the physical environment plays. If you have ever worked in construction, you know that the "traditional" jobsite environment can be tough. Work in the field is hard, and, at times, conditions can be less than welcoming for some people. Over the years, I have noticed how inadequate jobsite conditions have led to bad outcomes. Working in cramped conditions, using dirty porta-potties, and resting in poorly created break areas make people unhappy. It was not until I joined DPR Self-perform that I understood the emotional and physical toll that these working conditions take on people.

I came to a simple conclusion: *People who feel valued, respected, and cared for do their best work.* My goal was to make respect and care visible in practical ways—not only through what we said, but through the conditions people experienced every day. Although building personal relationships with craftspeople and thanking them for their efforts is a great first step, taking actions to demonstrate that we, craft and admin, are ALL teammates is just as important if not more so.

While leading SPW, one of my first priorities was improving the basic jobsite facilities, those things that are easy to take for granted but matter a lot to the people who spend their days on-site. I remember walking onto job sites where the restrooms were dirty and poorly maintained. If we were serious about showing respect for people, then why were we still subjecting our teammates to these conditions? This was an area where I knew I could make an immediate impact. If we wanted our teams to feel respected, we needed to start by improving all those things they are exposed to on a daily basis: restrooms, break areas, and signage.

So, we made a change. In 2023, we started having real conversations as a Regional Leadership Team about making significant improvements to our jobsite conditions. We piloted supgraded facilities on several jobsites and began receiving positive responses from our craft teammates. In 2024, we rolled out an initiative to upgrade jobsite restrooms across our region. We replaced the portable toilets with modern restrooms (Figure 52) that have heat, air conditioning, and handwashing capabilities. This shift was not just about hygiene; it was about giving our craftspeople and trade partners the dignity they deserved.

The restroom upgrades were just the start. We also revamped our break areas (Figure 53), making sure they were comfortable and well-equipped—just like those for their admin counterparts. We provided tables, chairs, and microwaves so workers could eat, rest, and recharge. These improvements are not just about convenience but about showing people that we care about their wellbeing. Amenities like these can affect how people experience the jobsite and whether they feel considered in its design.

We displayed signage on our projects to introduce messages like "See Something, Say Something" and "Stand Together, Build Belonging." These were not just safety slogans but reminders that we were all in this together, and everyone's voice mattered. The signs reinforced the same message we were trying to demonstrate through improvements to the physical environment and through our everyday interactions.

The Business Case for Psychological Safety

Many leaders might look at these upgrades and think they are a luxury, an unnecessary cost. But for me, the business case is clear. *The conditions we create communicate what we value and how seriously we take people's wellbeing and belonging.* Today, it is just not enough to simply ensure that people feel like they are not in imminent physical danger; they need to feel like they belong and are a vital part of the team. A psychologically safe workforce is more engaged, safer, and more likely to stay. We have witnessed this firsthand on our projects.

I have also seen how the work environment can affect whether people raise what they are seeing in the field—from unsafe conditions and quality issues to coordination problems, unclear direction, or opportunities to improve the work. For me, that is part of the deeper business value: surfacing those things early, while there is still time to respond.

Improved facilities and visible messages support psychological safety by communicating care, respect, and attention to people's daily experience. They are meaningful, but they are not sufficient on their own. Their contribution is reinforced by respectful interactions, meaningful responses to concerns, and consistent effort from leaders and team members.

Figure 52 Upgraded Temporary Bathrooms Include Toilets, Sinks with Running Water, Heating and Cooling, and Privacy (Courtesy of DPR Construction).

Figure 53 Construction Project Break Area (Courtesy of DPR Construction).

Leading With Self

As a leader, I have learned that I must model the behavior I want to see in others. If I want my team to speak up, I must show them that I'm willing to do the same and that I am actively listening to them.

One of the stories that stand out to me happened on a project where a staffing decision I was not entirely aligned with was about to be made. The team was trying to respond to real project pressures and keep the work moving, and one idea on the table was to keep the schedule moving by working Sundays. While the intention was to support the project, I felt that asking people to stretch even further was not the right answer. In the past, I might have just gone along with it and kept my concerns to myself to keep the project moving. However, as my understanding of psychological safety developed, I knew remaining silent was not the right approach anymore.

This was an opportunity to model the behavior I wanted other team members to embrace. Instead of keeping these concerns to myself, I called a team meeting and opened the discussion. I wanted everyone to weigh the tradeoffs, not just accept the fastest answer. It was not an easy conversation, but it was the right one. People shared their perspectives openly, and because we created space for that discussion, we reached a better decision—one that took care of our people and improved the project. For me, that was a turning point. It reshaped how I understood leadership and psychological safety. I realized that leadership is not only about inviting others to speak but also about being willing to speak yourself and model that behavior, especially when silence would be easier.

As I continued leading the SPW team at DPR, I realized that speaking up myself was only part of the responsibility. I also had to make sure others had the space to share what they were seeing, ask questions, challenge my thinking, and tell me when something was not working. I remember once being called out by one of my team members for not listening closely enough. It stung, but it was a wake-up call. I realized that as a leader, I had to actively listen to every team member, not just the loudest voices. Some of the most valuable insights come from the quietest corners of the jobsite, and I needed to make sure those voices were given the same attention.

I admit my journey with psychological safety has not always been easy. At times, I have found myself slipping back into old habits, being too direct or focused on getting things done quickly. Leading well requires me to notice when this happens and stay intentional about how I show up, especially under pressure. One of the ways I encourage my team to speak up is by sharing my own mistakes. I'm open about the challenges I have faced and how I have worked to overcome them, with the support of my team. I have found that being open about my own experiences makes it easier for others to bring their concerns, ideas, or feedback to me.

Leading With Empathy

The biggest change I have seen in my leadership journey is learning to lead with empathy. As a leader, I always try to put myself in the shoes of my craft workers and team members. *If I were on the jobsite every day, how would I want to feel? What conditions would I need to thrive?* The answer is simple: I want to feel valued. I want to feel that my leadership cares about both my wellbeing and my success.

That is the approach I have taken when encouraging my direct team to speak up and tackle sensitive issues. I encourage open communication by demonstrating empathy and showing that I'm there to support them. Whether it is a small issue or a more significant problem, I make it clear that I'm open to hearing what they have to say and that their voice matters.

For all leaders, especially those who are just starting to explore psychological safety, my advice is simple: *Put yourself in your team's shoes*. Think about how you would want to feel if you were in their position. Would you feel valued? Would you feel heard? How would you feel coming onto the site every day as a result? Start there and make that visible in how you lead. Do not just talk about it, live it. Model the behavior you want to see in your team. Create spaces for them to speak up, ask questions, and offer feedback. Small changes—from better facilities to making time to listen—can shape how people experience working together.

Leadership is a journey, and you will never have all the answers. But if you help create the conditions for psychological safety—where your team feels heard, respected, and empowered to contribute—you are laying the foundation for a stronger, more resilient team. At DPR, we are committed to making psychological safety a core part of our culture. That commitment is reflected in how we lead, work together, and respond when people speak up.

8.2 Moments That Make—or Break—Voice

Psychological safety is built in real time—whenever someone raises a concern, asks a question, admits uncertainty, or offers a different perspective. The question is: *what happens next?*

Taken together, these stories show how psychological safety takes shape across many kinds of leadership moments: when a leader receives unwelcome information, offers difficult feedback, recognizes a contribution, notices silence, responds to a concern, improves conditions that affect people's dignity, or chooses to speak when staying quiet would be easier. What happens in those moments influences what people bring forward next time and whether "we" becomes real in how the team works together. In each, the choices leaders make can strengthen or weaken voice:

- When someone stops work or raises a concern, the team can respond with appreciation and curiosity—or irritation and dismissal.
- When someone admits uncertainty, asks for help, or owns a mistake, the response can focus on learning—or blame.
- When someone offers a different perspective or questions the current plan, the idea can be explored—or treated as resistance.
- When feedback is shared, it can focus on behavior and improvement—or become personal and punitive.
- When pressure rises, the team can reinforce shared ownership through "we" language—or shift responsibility to "them."
- When workplace conditions reveal that people's needs have been overlooked, leaders can acknowledge and address the gap—or allow it to continue.

Paz presents psychological safety as a responsibility that begins with the leader. Through experiences of overwork and punished candor, she shows the importance of caring for yourself, understanding the people you support, giving honest feedback respectfully, and building the relationships and shared direction that allow people to contribute. Her story reminds us never to assume psychological safety already exists; it requires intentional attention as people, roles, and teams change.

Nick shows how psychological safety moves from a set of values into everyday leadership practice. He connects stop-work authority with thoughtful feedback, regular check-ins, visible recognition through programs, and the responsibility to coach other leaders. His story reminds us that psychological safety cannot rest on policies or words alone; it is reinforced when leaders listen, care about people beyond their performance, recognize their contributions, remain open to feedback, and model the behaviors they expect from others.

Stephen focuses on vulnerability and deliberate design. His account of a team remaining silent after a project executive introduced an unclear reporting change shows why silence cannot be treated as agreement and why power dynamics and meeting structure matter. By pairing that lesson with an example of bringing decision-makers closer to the craftworkers doing the work, he shows how leaders can make it easier for questions and feedback to surface, listen in ways that influence decisions, normalize feedback in all directions, and combine grace with clear accountability.

Jack makes respect tangible. From responding when a craftworker was threatened with termination to improving jobsite facilities, and learning to listen more carefully to voices that might otherwise be overlooked, he shows that psychological safety is shaped by both everyday interactions and working conditions. His story reminds leaders to act when people's dignity is compromised, demonstrate care in visible ways, model speaking up themselves, and listen with empathy so people feel valued and able to contribute.

Leaders are constantly shaping the *cost of voice*.

Sometimes leaders **lower** that cost by:

- Responding with curiosity instead of defensiveness.
- Treating questions and differing perspectives as useful instead of inconvenient.
- Making space for clarification and negotiation before commitment.
- Following through when concerns are raised.
- Modeling vulnerability by acknowledging uncertainty and mistakes.
- Giving honest feedback with care and respect.
- Creating different ways for people to contribute when speaking up openly feels difficult.
- Demonstrating through action that people matter.

Sometimes leaders **raise** that cost by:

- Reacting with irritation, ridicule, or punishment.
- Treating silence as agreement.
- Treating disagreement as resistance or disloyalty.
- Embarrassing people in public.
- Leaving concerns unresolved.
- Failing to address workplace interactions or conditions that send the message that the work matters more than the people doing it.

Over time, these responses shape whether people believe it is safe to take the next step:

Safe to ask.
Safe to clarify.
Safe to disagree.
Safe to stop work.
Safe to admit a mistake.
Safe to share an idea.
Safe to give feedback.
Safe to name a concern before it becomes costly.
Safe to do all of this and still know they belong.

When leaders respond with respect, curiosity, steadiness, and follow-through, people learn that speaking up leads to action. It may lead to clarity. It may lead to support. It may lead to a better decision, a better plan, or a better way of working. Even when the requested action cannot be taken, leaders can explain why and close the loop.

When leaders respond with dismissal, blame, indifference, or silence, people learn something else: protect yourself first. Important information surfaces late—or not at all—showing up as rework, hidden frustration, bad handoffs, preventable errors, poor morale, and missed opportunities to learn.

Table 11 Leadership Practices That Support Speaking Up

Practice	*What It Looks Like in Action*
Make Speaking Up an Explicit Expectation	State clearly that raising concerns, stopping unsafe work, asking questions, and surfacing risks early are expected parts of the job—not disruptions to it.
Listen with curiosity	Give people your attention, ask questions to understand, and stay open to what they are saying—especially when the message is difficult or challenges your perspective.
Make feedback routine	Use regular check-ins, coaching moments, and follow-up conversations so feedback can flow both ways and become normal, specific, and developmental rather than sudden or threatening.
Treat silence like data	Notice when people stop talking, hesitate, or defer too quickly. Ask what may be unclear, risky, or hard to say in that moment.
Design meetings for voice	Use smaller groups, written input, pauses for clarification, and explicit invitations to name risks, constraints, or uncertainty before decisions are made.
Recognize what is worth reinforcing	Acknowledge people's efforts, contributions, and behaviors that support the team. Be specific about what they did and why it mattered.
Model vulnerability while maintaining accountability	Admit when you do not know, own mistakes, and ask for help—while still keeping expectations clear and following through on commitments.
Protect dignity	Respond to mistakes, uncertainty, and disagreement without blame or embarrassment.
	Act quickly when someone is treated disrespectfully. Improve conditions that signal respect in practical ways. Let the environment communicate, "You matter here."
Close loops on concerns	When someone raises an issue, respond, clarify next steps, and return to it. Closing the loop helps people see how their input was considered, even when the final decision differs from what they proposed.
Reinforce the language of "we"	Speak in ways that strengthen shared ownership: our work, our risk, our learning, our responsibility.

What stood out in these stories was the choices these leaders made in everyday moments: creating space for people to speak, listening when they did, responding with respect, showing care, acknowledging their own mistakes, and following through on what they heard.

Table 11 turns these stories into behaviors you can practice. These are the daily practices that make truth easier to tell, learning easier to sustain, and One Team more likely to hold under pressure.

8.3 Closing Reflections

If this book has made one idea clear, it is this: teams do not become healthier by accident. They become healthier because people, especially leaders, shape the conditions that make healthier behavior possible.

By now, you have seen that psychological safety is not separate from the other themes in this book. It is woven through all of them.

- It is tied to respect because people speak more honestly when they feel their dignity is intact.
- It is tied to learning because teams learn faster when people can admit what they do not know, surface mistakes, and adjust.

- It is tied to caring because support becomes real when people can ask for help without shame.
- It is tied to listening because speaking up is more likely to continue when it is met with attention, curiosity, and care.
- It is tied to promises because reliable commitments require room for clarification, negotiation, and truth.

That is why leadership matters so much. Leaders do not only manage work but also help shape the emotional and relational conditions under which the work gets done.

And that leaves each leader with a practical question:

What am I doing, consistently, that makes it safer and more worthwhile for people to tell the truth here?

Use the questions below not as a checklist but as a way to choose where your leadership needs to become more intentional.

1. Where does voice become expensive on my team?
   - In which settings do people become more careful, more filtered, or more silent? Is it in large meetings? Around certain leaders? Under schedule pressure? Around certain topics?
   - Start by identifying the places where truth becomes harder to tell. Those are the places in which leadership design matters most.
2. What response are people learning to expect from me?
   - When someone raises a risk, asks a question, disagrees, or admits a mistake, what do I usually communicate in that moment? Curiosity? Irritation? Appreciation? Defensiveness? Impatience?
   - People do not learn whether it is safe to speak from what leaders say they value. They learn it from patterns in how leaders respond.
3. Where do I need to make the next step safer?
   - Safer to clarify. Safer to say, "I do not know." Safer to stop work. Safer to challenge a plan. Safer to raise a concern before it becomes costly.
   - Consider what you can change in these moments to reduce hesitation and make speaking up easier.
4. What structure or routine would make honesty easier here?
   - Would a weekly check-in help? A better close to meetings? A written input option? A clearer invitation to name constraints before committing?
   - Psychological safety is reinforced when teams build opportunities for voice into the way they work rather than leaving them to chance.
5. What is one practical change I can make in the next 30 days to help people feel valued and respected?
   - What would help people feel more respected in the environment where they work every day? It may be a physical improvement. It may be access, hygiene, recovery space, signage, onboarding, or the way people are greeted and spoken to.
   - Dignity is made visible through the conditions people experience and the way they are treated every day.

6. Where do I need to listen differently?
   - Who do I hear from most often? Who am I not hearing from? Who may benefit from more time, a different format, or a direct invitation to contribute?
   - Listening requires creating genuine opportunities to contribute, rather than relying only on those who speak most readily.
7. What behavior do I need to model more visibly?
   - Admitting uncertainty? Owning mistakes? Giving and being open to feedback? Asking for help? Responding promptly when disrespect is reported or observed?
   - People pay attention to what leaders do. When leaders consistently practice the behaviors they expect from others, those behaviors are more likely to take hold across the team.
8. What is one commitment I will revisit—not just announce?
   - Choose one behavior, one routine, or one condition you will improve. Make it specific. Make it visible. Return to it.
   - Follow-through is what turns leadership intentions into something people can experience.

In the end, the question is not whether leaders believe psychological safety is important. Most do. The real question is whether people can feel it in the way work is led.

Can they ask when they do not know?
Can they speak before the problem gets bigger?
Can they disagree without becoming outsiders?
Can they stop the work, name the risk, admit the mistake, or ask for help—and still remain fully part of the team?

Beneath it all sits the deeper question this whole book has been building toward:

Is "we" real here?

Not in language alone.
Not in value statements written on the wall.
Not in a speech at kickoff.
But in the meeting.
In the field.
In the handoff.
In the response to bad news.
In the way people are treated when the work gets hard.

"We" becomes real when people can ask for help without paying a social price.
When concerns are welcomed rather than quietly brushed aside.
When mistakes and breakdowns lead to learning rather than blame.
When commitments are made clearly and honored reliably.
When people support one another and protect the team's work, not just their own.
When performance does not come at the expense of people.

Lead so that "we" becomes something people can trust.
Make it safer. Make it more worthwhile—together, as *One Team*.

Acknowledgments

This book was written in the middle of life—between work, research, travel, motherhood, and all the invisible responsibilities that continue whether or not a manuscript is due. Because of that, this book carries far more than my voice. It carries the love, sacrifice, patience, and belief of the people who made it possible.

My daughters, Emilia and Victoria, are at the center of that. Writing this book required hours that might otherwise have belonged to them—hours of playing together and being present for the ordinary moments that matter so much. I took that time because I believed this book needed to exist. And yet, even when I came to them with too little time and too much on my mind, they met me with love. Lately, as I have started traveling more, I can feel how much they miss me and how hard it is for them to let me go. I carry that with me. One day, when they are old enough to read this book, I hope they feel proud of their mama. More than anything, I hope they feel how deeply they were loved through all of it.

My mom, Julia, has been with me through this entire journey. In so many ways, she has helped raise my daughters so I could continue working, mentoring students, growing, and bringing this book to life. What she has given through her care and dedication is difficult to put into words. Watching how much a mother can hold, give, and sustain has been one of the greatest lessons of my life. This book rests on more of her love than most people will ever know.

My partner in life, Kevin, carried so much of the weight of our home and our children while I worked to finish this manuscript. I am deeply thankful for the many times he stepped in, took on more, and gave me the space to keep going. Books like this are never the work of one person alone, even when only one or two names appear on the cover.

One of the most meaningful parts of writing this book has been sharing the journey with Glenn Ballard. Over the last couple of years, we spent countless weekly calls working to bring it to the finish line. He is not only my co-author but also my advisor, and his influence on my thinking is woven throughout these pages. I am deeply grateful for his guidance, his patience, his belief in this work, and his partnership throughout the process.

DPR Construction shaped much of what One Team came to mean to me. When I was applying to graduate school and approached DPR with the idea of working on psychological safety to improve how we manage quality on our job sites, I was met with trust. That trust changed my life. DPR supported me through my PhD journey and gave me the opportunity to work closely with project teams, learn from them, and help create conditions where they could speak up more openly. So much of what I understand about healthy teams was not learned from theory alone but through real people doing real work and trying to build something better together. At DPR, We Exist to Build Great Things®.

The leaders who shared their stories in this book—Paz Arroyo, Nick Loughrin, Jack Poindexter, and Stephen Terni—did more than contribute examples. They helped ground the book in lived practice. I invited them into these pages because I have seen firsthand how they practice what this book is trying to describe. Their stories brought credibility, honesty, and heart to the work.

My student, Mauricio Neyra, made this book better through his thoughtful feedback and insights, especially around visuals. His perspective helped sharpen ideas that I hope will now be clearer and more useful to our readers.

Sean Graystone generously read an early draft and offered careful feedback that helped strengthen the manuscript. What meant even more was his encouragement along the way—his belief that this work needed to be written and that these were things that needed to be said. That kind of affirmation stayed with me. I am deeply grateful for the care, attention, and support he gave this book.

I also think of Ralph Romayor, Flavio Villanueva, Rafael Castro, Omar Alfaro, Walter Melendez, and Santiago Ruiz with deep gratitude. They believed in me at times when I could not yet see how far I might go. Their belief became part of the foundation that carried me forward.

Amy Edmondson's work also lives behind these pages in an important way. Her scholarship gave language, legitimacy, and direction to questions that mattered deeply to me. In many ways, she helped me see that the social conditions around work are not secondary to performance; they shape it. Her work inspired this journey and helped open a path that eventually led to this book.

This book may carry my name, but it was built through the care, trust, sacrifice, and encouragement of many people. I did not get here alone, and I would never want to tell the story that way.

—Sulyn

Bibliography

Brown, B. (2018). *Dare to Lead: Brave Work. Tough Conversations. Whole Hearts*. New York: Random House Books.

Burris, E. R., Detert, J. R., and Chiaburu, D. S. (2008). "Quitting before Leaving: The Mediating Effects of Psychological Attachment and Detachment on Voice." *Journal of Applied Psychology*, 93(4), 912–922.

Deming, W. E. (1993). *The New Economics for Industry, Government, Education*. MIT Center for Advanced Engineering Study.

Detert, J. R., and Edmondson, A. C. (2011). "Implicit Voice Theories: Taken-for-Granted Rules of Self-Censorship at Work." *Academy of Management Journal*, 54(3), 461–488.

Edmondson, A. C. (1999). "Psychological Safety and Learning Behavior in Work Teams." *Administrative Science Quarterly*, 44(2), 350–383.

Edmondson, A. C. (2018). *The Fearless Organization: Creating Psychological Safety in the Workplace for Learning, Innovation, and Growth*. Hoboken, NJ: John Wiley & Sons.

Edmondson, A. C. (2023). *Right Kind of Wrong: The Science of Failing Well*. Hoboken, NJ: Simon and Schuster.

Edmondson, A. C., and Lei, Z. (2014). "Psychological Safety: The History, Renaissance, and Future of an Interpersonal Construct." *Annual Review of Organizational Psychology and Organizational Behavior*, 1(1), 23–43.

Flores, F. (1982). *Management and Communication in the Office of the Future*. Doctoral Dissertation. Berkeley, CA: University of California.

Gomez Villanueva, S. (2023). *Behavior-Based Quality System (BBQS)*. Doctoral Dissertation. Berkeley, CA: University of California.

Gomez Villanueva, S., Bishop, B., Ballard, G., Saenz, M., and Tommelein, I. D. (2019). "An Active Caring Approach Through Psychological Safety in Construction Projects." *Proceedings of the 27th Annual Conference of the International Group for Lean Construction*, Dublin, Ireland, 1037–1048.

Hanna, E., Gough, B., and Markham, S. (2020). "Masculinities in the Construction Industry: A Double-Edged Sword for Health and Wellbeing?" *Gender, Work & Organization*, 27(4), 632–646.

Kahn, W. A. (1990). "Psychological Conditions of Personal Engagement and Disengagement at Work." *Academy of Management Journal*, 33(4), 692–724.

Lloyd Smith, J., Meyerson, D., and Walling, S. J. (2016). *Strategic Play: The Creative Facilitator's Guide Volume #2*. Wordzworth Publishing.

Macomber, H., and Howell, G. A. (2003). "Linguistic Action: Contributing to the Theory of Lean Construction." *Proceedings of the 11th Annual Conference of the International Group for Lean Construction*, Virginia, USA.

Marquet, L. D. (2013). *Turn the Ship Around! A True Story of Turning Followers into Leaders*. Penguin.

Schein, E. H., and Bennis, W. (1965). *Personal and Organizational Change Through Group Methods*. New York: Wiley.

Schroeder, J., Risen, J. L., Gino, F., and Norton, M. I. (2019). "Handshaking Promotes Deal-Making by Signaling Cooperative Intent." *Journal of Personality and Social Psychology*, 116(5), 743–768.

Appendix

Questions to Assess Team Psychological Safety and Behavioral Dynamics

	Team Psychological Safety
With respect to the team leader	• I am able to bring up problems and tough issues to my team leader. • If I make a mistake while doing my work on this team, I feel safe speaking up to my team leader. • My skills and talents are valued and utilized by my team leader. • If I have concerns or questions about my work, I feel safe reaching out to my team leader. • The leader of this team is understanding when I make a mistake and does not use it against me. • When I make a mistake, the leader of this team helps me to correct it. • It is difficult to ask my team leader for help. (R) • I feel safe making suggestions and offering feedback to my team leader.
With respect to team members	• I am able to bring up problems and tough issues to my team members. • If I make a mistake while doing my work on this team, I feel safe speaking up to my team members. • My skills and talents are valued and used by my team members. • If I have concerns or questions about my work, I feel safe reaching out to my team members. • My team members are understanding when I make a mistake and do not use it against me. • When I make a mistake, my team members help me to correct it. • It is difficult to ask my team members for help. (R) • I feel safe making suggestions and offering feedback to my team members.
Team Voice	• When I have questions or ideas that can contribute to what my team is doing, I . . . (Silence scale: Always stay silent to Never stay silent) • When I have stayed silent when working with this team, it is typically because of . . . (Fear, Futility, Both) • What can your team do to strengthen psychological safety? Consider what would help team members contribute openly, ask questions, share concerns, seek help, and learn from mistakes. (Open-ended question).

Note: Unless otherwise indicated, all items use a 7-point Likert scale, from 1 (strongly disagree) to 7 (strongly agree). Items marked (R) are reverse-scored questions.

(Continued)

	Behavioral Dynamics
Being Respectful	• Members of my team treat others fairly. • Members of my team help others develop their skills. • Members of my team communicate professionally, even when they disagree or discuss challenging issues. • Members of my team value others' expectations and perspectives. • Members of my team are recognized and acknowledged for their efforts and achievements. • Members of my team are inclusive and welcoming, regardless of differences in background, opinion, skills, or expertise. • Members of my team address disrespectful behavior when it occurs.
Active Caring	• Members of my team go out of their way to help one another. • Members of my team consider how their decisions and actions may affect others. • Members of my team take pride in each other's accomplishments and actively celebrate successes together. • The team acknowledges and appreciates individuals who demonstrate behaviors that support and uplift others. • Members of my team regularly check in with each other.
Making Reliable Promises	• Members of my team honor their commitments. • Before making a commitment, members check scope, capacity, and constraints to ensure the work is achievable. • When a promise is at risk, members communicate early about the issue and work with others to adjust. • Members of my team feel safe to say "no" or "not yet" when a request cannot or should not be done. • Members of my team follow up on commitments and communicate when they have been completed. • When a commitment is missed, members of my team work together to understand what happened and determine the next step.
Speaking Up	• Members of my team speak up if they feel a plan or idea will not work. • Members of my team openly acknowledge when they do not know something so they can get help. • Members of my team say something when they do not understand a decision, instruction, or expectation. • Members of my team share early warnings (near misses, small issues) before they become big problems. • Members of my team speak up when actions conflict with our goals or values. • Members of my team actively encourage and support each other to voice their ideas and perspectives.
Being Diligent	• Before starting a task or project, members of my team make sure each person understands their role and responsibilities. • Members of my team assess readiness before executing a task (e.g., by making sure information is up-to-date, resources are available). • Before starting work, members of my team make sure that expectations are clear, achievable, and appropriate. • Members of my team create a shared vision of the desired end outcome before starting a task. • Members of my team follow established processes to ensure thorough planning and preparation before and during work. • Members of my team pay attention to details in both planning and carrying out tasks. • Members of my team verify that completed work meets expectations before it is handed off to others.

(*Continued*)

(Continued)

Active Listening	• Members of my team ask questions and promote discussions to better understand diverse perspectives. • Members of my team listen without interrupting. • Members of my team listen to understand rather than simply waiting for their turn to respond. • Members of my team pay attention and avoid distractions during conversations. • Members of my team use verbal and nonverbal cues to show engagement during conversations. • Members of my team confirm their understanding; for example, by paraphrasing ("Here is what I heard . . .").
Active Learning	• Members of my team offer ideas and solutions when challenges or problems arise. • Members of my team share knowledge and resources so others can learn. • Members of my team regularly review what is helping or hurting the team's performance. • Members of my team learn from mistakes and take steps to avoid repeating them. • Members of my team are encouraged to test new approaches and learn from the results. • Members of my team learn from what went well and apply this to future endeavors. • Members of my team ask for feedback and act on it.
Strengthening Team Behavioral Dynamics	• What can your team do to strengthen active learning, active listening, diligence, speaking up, reliable promises, active caring, and respect? (Open-ended question).
	Performance and Wellbeing
Performance	• This team keeps getting better. • This team consistently achieves its goals. • This team uses its collective knowledge and capabilities to produce better results. • Overall, I am satisfied with the performance of this team.
Wellbeing	• I can be myself when working with this team. • I can do my best work on this team without compromising my wellbeing. • I feel a sense of belonging on this team. • I feel energized rather than drained by my experience working with this team. • Working with this team has a positive effect on my wellbeing. • My overall sense of wellbeing when working with this team is . . . (very poor, poor, fair, neutral, good, very good, excellent).

Index

Note: Page numbers in **bold** refer to images or tables.

www.ingramcontent.com/pod-product-compliance
Lightning Source LLC
LaVergne TN
LVHW060533111026
849885LV00035B/366

* 9 7 8 1 0 4 1 2 2 4 5 5 6 *